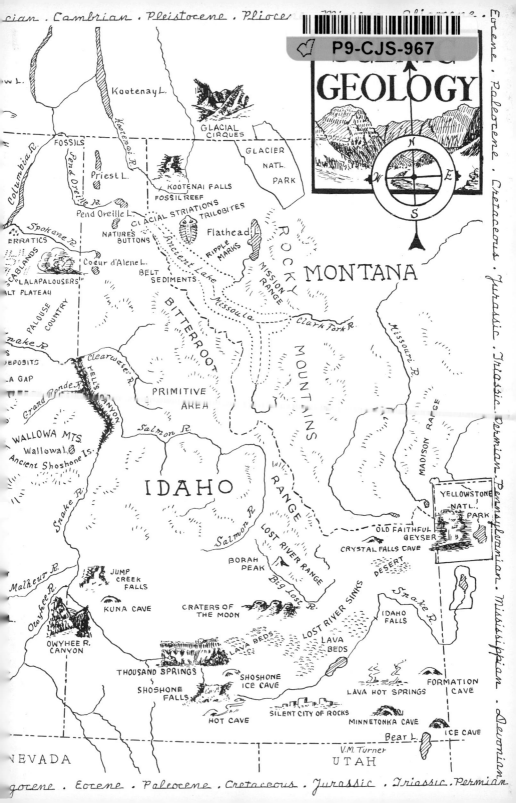

SCENIC GEOLOGY

OF THE PACIFIC NORTHWEST

SCENIC

GEOLOGY

Portland   •   Oregon   •   1962

OF THE PACIFIC NORTHWEST

by Leonard C. Ekman

edited by L. K. Phillips

BINFORDS & MORT, *Publishers*

PREFACE

The portion of the earth's surface known as the Pacific Northwest has an exciting story for those interested in its geologic history and character. Furrowed, wrinkled, and sometimes grotesque landscapes reveal how mountains and hills were molded and carved, how drainage patterns in gravel and stone were etched by streams and rivers, and even how the land itself was slowly formed. The fascinating story of this region breaks through all around us.

An old shoreline tells where waves of a bygone century lapped on quiet, lifeless shores. A road-cut exposes the materials which there make up the earth's crust. Crystalline rock along the ramparts of a snow-capped peak shows that once a fiery, molten mass welled up from earth's depths, here to become solid stone. Unsorted gravel in a U-shaped valley records glacial times when deep ice scoured mountain rock and trenched the land. Whether seen through a picture window, or experienced underfoot on a mountain trail, a bit of landscape will disclose some part of earth's drama.

With its manifold landscape patterns, the geology of the Pacific Northwest rivals in interest that of any other region in the world.

In Alaska is the largest number of active glaciers to be found anywhere on American soil. Mount McKinley—Paul Bunyan of the Alaska Range— looks down on other towering peaks, all splendid examples of glaciers and their work. The same earth forces at work everywhere on the globe have periodically—and dramatically—altered and rearranged this Land of the Midnight Sun. Here on display are the sediments of rivers and sea, and volcanic regions formed long ago by violent upheaval. Permafrost—perennially frozen ground—grips vast areas of Alaska. This is a perpetual challenge to builders on the land.

Ribbed north and south by the lofty Cascades and the storied Canadian Rockies, British Columbia embraces a virgin wilderness of sharply eroded peaks, beautiful mountain lakes, sparkling streams —ready to be explored and enjoyed. Its coast, with long, finger-like embayments reaching far in from the sea, lures those who would explore this scenic area by water. Here is a land scarred by glaciers, and at times warped and tilted into mountains that shoulder out the sky.

In Washington State, the northern Cascades exhibit both igneous granites and the ancient sediments elevated by them. Here majestic Mount Rainier rises, still wearing its cloak of ancient glaciers, still mantled with perpetual snow. This ice-tentacled sentinel is visible to the approaching tourist for scores of miles. Farther west, across glaciated Puget Sound, are the untamed Olympics, skirted by the giant spruce of the shadow-filled rain forest—and not yet fully explored. To the east lies the massive eruption of the Columbia Plateau, with its layer upon layer of somber basalt. Through a portion of this runs the scar made by the rampaging Columbia in the closing days of the Pleistocene—the Grand Coulee, one of the world's greatest water-eroded channels.

Travel any direction in Oregon and you will discover that this state is a natural wonderland. If you seek volcanoes, caves, sand dunes, fossils, gem stones—it has all of these, and more. The John Day country is a storehouse for one of the most extensive fossil collections in the world. It is a place where animals large and small once flourished near prehistoric lakes and swamps, later to be killed by erupting volcanoes in the high Cascades. The incredibly blue waters of Crater Lake in southwest Oregon are cupped in the cone of an extinct volcano. Out from Grants Pass are the Oregon Caves, often called the Marble Halls of Oregon. Prehistoric nature carved a myriad of exquisite and eerie forms in these limestone labyrinths.

Western Montana displays vast thicknesses of sedimentary rock, now folded and broken into formidable cliffs and steep escarpments. These sediments tell the area washed by the inland sea which, in eons gone by, covered this region. Clark Fork Valley once held Lake Missoula, likely the greatest impoundment of glacial water of all time. Farther north and east in Glacier National Park is a jumbled array of sharp peaks and deep valleys— the result of faulting, glaciation, and severe upthrust of bedded rock.

Idaho also is rich in scenic geology. Belt sediments like those of western Montana appear in the northern part of the state. Their block-faulted arrangement shows on the cliff faces of the mountains in the Panhandle. Among Idaho's landscape treasures is its Craters of the Moon, a showcase of recent volcanics in a setting of ancient rock. Nearby, two rivers—swallowed in porous lava beds—travel mysteriously underground. Both hot and cold springs gush from Idaho's land forms, and there are more lakes in this state than have ever been counted, despite much semiarid land. In the wilderness area of central Idaho lie lakes that have been viewed only from the air. Some of the state's abundant water supply passes over such spectacular falls as Shoshone, the Niagara of the West.

In the Pacific Northwest are several scenic and geologically interesting rivers. The mighty Columbia has a history involving struggle against glaciation, lava flows, and a rising mountain barrier. The Snake and Salmon are deep canyon rivers, so deep that only in a few places is footing possible on their precipitous walls. These massive trenches offer some of the most awesome scenery in the West.

Scenic Geology of the Pacific Northwest attempts to make the region's landscape more meaningful whether viewed from the automobile, the airplane, or on foot; and more interesting if used as a guide for those who seek the story of the land on which they live and over which they may hope to travel some day. Perhaps the reader will find how to interpret his own geologic community and its particular drama in earth and stone.

My sincere thanks go to all those who have helped in the preparation of this book: to those who have lent me photographs, and to those with whom I was associated in geology as a student and as a fellow worker.

Leonard C. Ekman

CONTENTS

people destroyed by Mazama . . . Newberry Crater
. . . East and Paulina lakes . . . Newberry obsidian
. . . Fort Rock . . . The Three Sisters . . . Future of
the Cascades . . . Columbia Plateau . . . Grand Coulee
. . . McKenzie lava flows . . . Dry Falls . . . Lava
River Caves . . . Columnar structure . . . Craters of
the Moon . . . aa and pahoehoe . . . Dome volcanoes
. . . Composite volcanoes . . . Hot springs.

SCENIC GEOLOGY

OF THE PACIFIC NORTHWEST

Chapter 1

THE EARTH'S CRUST

The Pacific Northwest has many land forms and, among these land forms, myriad variations. Whether beautiful or grotesque, violent or passive — all find their patterns in the materials composing them.

A statue chiseled from marble may closely resemble one done in clay and both may be lovely, but, if equally exposed to the elements, the marble statue will be standing when the clay has crumbled. So it is with the materials of the earth. Some are soft, some hard, yet all are formed into shapes characteristic of themselves. Hard rocks weather differently from softer materials, their forms contrasting markedly.

Beyond it all rises the eternal question — what caused the earth's surface to begin its endless process of change?

We are told that our world began as a fiery ball, born out of the limitless firmament of burning gases and minerals. According to the astronomers, this newly-formed planet adopted an orbit and whirled away into space to become a world of cooling stone, void of plant and animal life.

These conditions would have remained permanent and the earth's surface as we know it, with its fascinating collection of living things, would never have existed—except for the surrounding layer of air. This gave the earth a unique position in the family of planets. The air tempers the direct rays of the sun, holding the sun-derived warmth as protection against the cold. In contrast, the moon has no atmosphere. It is a cold, barren sphere with extensive deserts and craters, which resemble extinct volcanoes; and sharp, non-eroded mountains. With no air or cloud insulation, the moon is fiercely hot in the daytime and bitterly cold at night.

Air is responsible for most of the changes through which the earth has passed. As it was warmed by the sun, then cooled by its passage over uneven parts of the earth, moisture was formed through condensation. This moisture, falling as rain and snow, became the first agent of destruction— and also of construction. With water at work on its surface, the earth began face-lifting operations soon after its creation.

Sedimentary Rock

Water running from higher to lower areas gradually attacked the rock over which it ran. Soon fine particles were carried downstream to be deposited at lower elevations. The destructive work of streams became easier as the freezing and thawing at high elevations caused more and more rock to crack and break.

Into the basins, which became the first lakes and oceans, drifted rock flour gathered from faraway areas. Layer by layer, this sediment — some fine, some coarse — was spread over the beds of lakes, ponds and oceans, and along the broad valleys where slow-moving water could no longer carry its load. Then came another change. From the weight of the accumulated mud and from pressure caused by the shifting of great sections of earth, the sediments hardened into stone. By uplift, great seas were drained — and the cutting power of streams, which went to work to carry away the sediments a second time, exposed the silt-covered basins. Layers of rock, piled in delicately-colored tiers, or tilted in striped array, were thus exposed. This sedimentary rock lures many a camera fan.

Examples of sedimentary rock are common. Sandstone, a popular building material, consists of sand particles cemented together. Shale, which often breaks into slabs of even thickness, is mere hardened clay or some other kind of mud. The flagstone walk winding through a garden may once have been oozy mud on a dark ocean floor. Sediment of pebbles, rocks and boulders cemented by finer material, is known as conglomerate. Oftentimes sedimentary rock holds fossils which help reconstruct the flora and fauna of ages past.

Western Montana and the panhandle of Idaho, both long ago covered by an inland sea, have extensive beds of sedimentary rock. Some of this rock is exposed in the John Day basin in central Oregon, where several areas of gaily-colored rock have been made into state parks. Those who learn to identify the bedded nature of this rock will notice that it is found scattered throughout the Pacific Northwest.

Igneous Rock

The interior of the earth is very hot because not all of the chemical reactions with which it was born have as yet been dissipated. In some parts of its interior the heat is still so great that rock has stayed in a molten state. When cooled, this molten material becomes igneous, or fiery, rock. Igneous rocks are composed of mineral crystals, some large, some microscopic. Because of its salt-and-pepper appear-

[3]

ance, granite is a good example of igneous rock and it is easily recognized.

A number of the spectacular landscapes in the Pacific Northwest have an igneous origin. Ages before man appeared on earth, deep cracks opened in the ground. From these poured liquid rock. Seeking the lowest level possible, this fiery mass filled all depressions in its path and, sweeping on, devoured everything before it. Lake bottoms were invaded. Rivers were pushed out of their channels, to hiss at the edge of the hot lava. Mountain canyons and even mountains themselves were often erased. Forests were engulfed, becoming charred and dead within the stone.

There are other examples of igneous action because molten rock is persistent in its travels. It exists between layers of weaker sedimentary rocks and even in cracks of other igneous materials. Some of it found — or made — enough room within the earth to form large masses, often extending for miles. Rocks that were forced aside pushed upward, where, exposed by erosion, they today form some of the great mountain ranges. Carved by glaciers and river wear, their snow-capped peaks make up some of the most scenic sights in western America.

Volcanoes, many of them still active, are another illustration of fire-formed rock. The lava ejected from one of them builds a monstrous duplicate of an ant hill, depositing blown-out materials in a circular pile around its mouth. Ash and rock fragments also are born of the volcano. Ashes, some known as pumice, have been found far from the roaring volcano which threw this popcorn-like substance to the winds. In the mountains which encircle Lake Chelan, a large deposit of pumice supplies the material for a chimney-block manufacturer. This deep layer of volcanic dust is fifty miles from its source, Glacier Peak, a snow-capped, extinct volcano in the State of Washington.

While sedimentary rocks are composed of cemented particles bedded in evenly-arranged layers, igneous rocks assume massive shapes made up of crystals of various forms. The rate at which the rock cooled determined the size of these igneous crystals. Large crystals in igneous materials show slow cooling; small crystals, rapid cooling. Some igneous rocks are so fine grained that they are actually glassy. This means that extremely rapid cooling took place when the rock hardened. In some areas, fluid lava entered lakes or rivers. This, of course, quickly chilled the molten rock. The Glass Buttes, composed of obsidian — a glass-like rock — are the result of fast-cooling lava. They appear along U. S. Highway 20, fifteen miles east of Hampton, Oregon.

The Pacific Northwest has an igneous history, the grandeur of its mountains being due to the collection of large masses of molten material below the earth. This later hardened and folded upward, where it disturbed many beds of previously-made sedimentary rocks to form a major part of the Northwest's vacation land. Such is the partial history of the beautiful Cascades, which extend northward from California across Oregon and Washington. Today these are broken into a startling array of peaks, sharp, jagged crests and bastions of sheer cliffs— flung along almost five hundred miles of mountain wilderness.

Crossing the Cascades is a motoring treat for Pacific Northwest residents. For the plains-reared person, it is a thrill long to be remembered. Beauty abounds at every season of the year. The deep snows of winter, the masses of flowers and the sparkling streams of spring, the bright green of summer, or the frost-painted leaves of fall, each makes the Cascade crossing—through any of the ten passes in Washington and Oregon—an unforgettable experience.

Still more igneous matter was added to the Cascades when nature in the Plio-Pleistocene studded this range with several minor volcanoes and five great ones—Mazama, Hood, St. Helens, Rainier and Baker. From these, molten rock spewed far out over the range that was their foundation. Finally, towering cones built up to become the picturesque, snow-covered sentinels familiar to thousands of Northwesterners. Other igneous mountains are abundant in the region. The Wallowas, the Blue Mountains, the Klamath Mountains and the Okanogan Highlands are all uplifted igneous masses. This rock has also entered the sedimentary beds of northern Idaho and western Montana. The difference in the rock is easily spotted by the absence of bedded layers in igneous areas.

A dark igneous rock known as b a s a l t covers southeastern Washington and parts of eastern Oregon and western Idaho. This welled up from subterranean chambers to spread over vast areas in the Northwest basin. It shows along nearly all east-west highways and is recognized by its massive layers with their fluted columns or highly-fractured faces, frequently weathered to a reddish brown.

Metamorphic Rock

A third kind of rock is interesting though less common in this area. It is metamorphic or changed rock. Originally this was either igneous or sedimentary. Not content just to pour mud into natural molds to form sedimentary slabs or to sluice melted rock into convenient openings, nature made this new, metamorphic rock. Heat and pressure produce it. As hot, igneous materials come into contact with other kinds of rock, underground baking occurs. When the degree of heat is high enough, some of the ingredients often melt, taking on different characteristics. In the presence of ground water, chemical changes occur; these determine the color and character of the rock.

A cook mixes flour, salt, milk, sugar, shortening, water and yeast into a kneaded dough. Heat changes this mixture into bread. By mixing, kneading and heating, the baker creates a new substance. Bread is unlike any of the carefully-measured ingredients of the uncooked dough. So it is with rock portions of the earth. Minerals in great variety are brought together by streams, glaciers, and the wind. Heat reduces these minerals into a new kind of rock. Chemical action of the air and water also changes them, often into striking colors and shapes.

Metamorphic rock is also produced when sediments of great weight are piled on already-deposited materials. Pressure changes the rock below. As nature arches its back, mountains rise, inch by inch, and rocks are twisted and crushed. Under such conditions, granite becomes banded and is called gneiss, and dull shale turns into the smooth slate used in classrooms. Limestone, first formed by the skeletons of sea animals hardened together under pressure, becomes the gleaming marble used in buildings or monuments.

Metamorphic rocks, however, occupy only a minor place in Northwest geology. They are widely and sparsely scattered along the predominant igneous and sedimentary regions. The granitic areas show where igneous rocks have been altered by pressure and contortion of the masses containing them. These are easily located in the Cascades and in the Okanogan Highlands because their particles are banded. Changed sedimentary rocks such as limestone and marble are found north of Spokane and on up to the Canadian border. Slate also appears here, whereas marble predominates in the Oregon Caves area.

In brief, these three kinds of rock are the substances seen about us every day. Some are very hard, some soft. Some, therefore, are easily worn by erosion, others are not. The curious observer need not travel far to find stories in rock and soil. They are as near as his garden or the outskirts of his town. A country drive will place him in the midst of provocative landscapes.

It has been said that "the mountains are here today, they were not here yesterday, they will not be here tomorrow." That is the business of uplift and destruction by erosion. We can see the materials of the landscape in the time of their youth and we can see them in the process of their aging. Many kinds of rock give color and shape to their surroundings. Even the smallest particle of rock has a history as old as the fiery earth, born out of the mysterious space of the heavens. Some of this rock has changed and some of this rock has moved great distances to build new land forms.

The entire Pacific Northwest is a geologic wonderland. All kinds of rock are close at hand and to be found in a variety of interesting forms. The region has undergone glaciation. It contains the sediments of ancient inundations. Volcanics as spectacular as those found anywhere in the world have played a part in its geologic history. The story of these

events is in the arrangement and character of today's rocks, which appear in myriad and challenging
display.

Chapter 2

TO BUILD A MOUNTAIN

Mountains are the stellar attractions among the many varieties of land forms of the Pacific Northwest. These cover a wide area, highly dissected by streams and glaciers; and many of them reach alpine elevations inaccessible to man. The possibility of setting foot on ground in some lofty, isolated area constantly lures both amateur and professional explorers.

The Cascades

The Cascade Mountains—a majestic north-south barrier extending from northern California through Oregon, Washington, and into British Columbia— attract a steady flow of visitors to marvel at their sharp peaks, their high, rock-rimmed snow fields, and the evergreen forests clothing their precipitous sides. Vacationists come to fish, to rest, to climb among their peaks and jumbled topography, their lakes, and mountain trails.

These mountains are more than a barrier to transportation routes. They form a wall against whose west side is lost most of the precipitation in the moisture-laden winds from the Pacific Ocean. These Cascades are responsible for the differences between the temperate climate to the west of them and the arid zone to the east. Because the erection of these mountains has created two opposite clim-

Photo No. 1

Wenatchee Daily World

The Cascade Range runs through Oregon, Washington, and British Columbia, an effective east-west barrier. Here is Stuart Lake in British Columbia, cradled in a cirque, one of the many places where snow has created a valley glacier. Note the deep scars cut by severe erosion on the slopes of these alp-like mountains.

ates, people living in Oregon and Washington cross them to seek the cooler air of the west side, or the dry air of the east side. "Going to the coast" and "going east of the mountains" are common expressions in these states. (Photo No. 1)

Geologists have climbed these peaks and have studied and photographed large portions of the vast range. In university laboratories, microscopes have revealed the various kinds of matter which compose this great western land form. Large portions of the Cascades must be explored to piece together the many events which have created them. That the story of these mountains is complex and widely scattered is proved by the great variety of rock materials with their hundreds of landscape patterns.

The area now occupied by the Cascade Mountains was once an ocean bottom. Through the geologic ages, nearly all land areas of the earth have at one time or another been submerged by the sea. Many areas along the Pacific Coast have such a history. In the case of the Cascades, the sea remained long enough to deposit great depths of mud and silt which in turn captured the remains of sea animals living on the ocean floor and in the water above it. Their fossils are frequently found in shale and limestone.

Next came tremendous but incredibly slow upheavals. Materials of the ocean bottom arched and cracked. It was at this time that the Cascades began their ascent as great masses of rock, tilted and twisted as if on the hinges of a gigantic door. Igneous action accompanied the uplift; and molten rock, welling up from the earth's interior, flooded into the fracture zones of the upheaving earth. When hardened, this fiery liquid formed a network of various thicknesses. In some areas it burst in angry explosions through the sedimentary layers which formed the roof of the uplifted mass, then flowed in avalanche-like streams down the slopes of the young Cascades. Later in the uplift period were formed the volcanoes which now appear on the crest of the range.

The Cascade Range came into existence during what is known as the Cascade Revolution. The range itself was only a minor part of the large uplift area. This revolution lasted a long time, beginning in the Miocene Age and ending in the Pleistocene—a span of several eons.

There is another chapter in the story of these mountains, the story of erosion. Surprisingly, the forces of erosion made the Cascades beautiful. Rain, collecting in streams whose yearly run-off is swollen by melting snow, etched the great rock walls in thousands of downward cuts. From the beginning of the Cascades to the present, these streams have deepened their channels. Year after year, as rock particles were loosened and carried away, the almost upright stream-cut scars have eaten into the body of the mammoth range.

In an age just passed, all the Cascades experienced valley glaciation, when valley bottoms were scoured and broadened. As ice disappeared, the debris of this glaciation became a part of the already-eroded region. Finally—still formidable but much lowered and bereft of most of its outer covering—the skeleton of its inner materials was laid bare. From these remains earth scientists have fitted together the story of the Cascades.

The story is still there for those who wish to discover it for themselves. The climber to the crest country may encounter sedimentary rocks, some containing fossils. These prove that the disturbance which created the Cascades acted first upon sediments; to some extent they mark the elevation of the mountains. Throughout the range, results of disturbance are clear. Faulting has displaced great sections of rock and, in some places, is responsible for the sheer cliffs.

In the Cascades, igneous rocks appear in a variety of positions, such as intruded materials in road-cuts and in many trailside formations. The prospector sinks his pick in these for signs of minerals. On the flanks of Cascade volcanoes, the material blown out or extruded in liquid form can be readily examined.

This range reaches its greatest width in British Columbia, beginning roughly at the Fraser River and continuing eastward for 125 miles. Crossing the Cascades in this latitude by air, or on one of two east-west highways, reveals many of the distinguishing features of the range's lofty grandeur. This northern end of the Cascades resembles a greatly eroded tableland with scattered groups of sharp peaks.

On the west side, in the Skagit Range, a series of peaks rises six to seven thousand feet in elevation. There are few trails in this area, but for those who disregard this inconvenience there are alpine meadows where heather and colorful alpine flowers soften the scars of streams and glaciers. In the central portion, where erosion has been severe, the peaks are more rounded. Sheer cliffs and many other landslide features are due to the precipitous slopes. The landslides have dammed streams and the resulting basins have in turn become lakes. Matterhorns, or cirque-bounded peaks, which have been almost totally consumed by glaciers, stand as rocky guardians at the American-Canadian Border. One of these, Mount Hozameen, with an elevation of 8080 feet, stands squarely on the boundary. It has the distinction of bearing this peaceful line through a rocky saddle, carved by ice long before boundaries were invented, or needed.

On the arid, eastern Okanogan portion, the Cascades have less forest covering and the slopes take on foothill character, but the exotic scenery has a come-visit-again influence. The northern extremity of the Cascades ends abruptly at the Plateau of British Columbia. Since this is several thousand feet lower, the geology applicable to the Cascades is no longer useful here—a new physiographic area has replaced the uplifted heights to the south.

The Cascade Mountains in Washington are really in two distinct parts, northern and southern. North of Snoqualmie Pass, a complex uplift of igneous rock, intermingled with sedimentary deposits, makes up one of the roughest alpine areas in America. It is here that a gigantic mass of once-fluid, granitic rock formed one of the most massive batholiths in the West. When it solidified and pushed upward, the sediments under which it rose were mildly distorted, much rock was metamorphosed, and then torn asunder by faulting and erosion, to make the northern Cascades a highly complex and often mysterious region.

Another interesting feature of the northern Washington Cascades is the uniform elevation of the peaks in this highly-eroded area. From the top of any of these mountains the horizon stretches level; few peaks rise over others. Mountain tops range from six to seven thousand feet above sea level. The tops of these uniform peaks represent the level of the old peneplain which existed at a much lower elevation before uplift and erosion went to work. This portion of the Cascades has been deeply scoured by valley glaciers. Cirques—or mountain recesses—on peaks and ridges can be counted in the hundreds. Ridges are sharp and slope steeply down into deep, timbered valleys. The result is one of the most beautiful alpine regions in America.

Between Stevens Pass and Snoqualmie Pass, the sharp-peak-deep-valley topography continues. The area can be entered from Snoqualmie Pass (elevation 3004 feet) on U. S. Highway 10, or from Stevens Pass (elevation 4061 feet) on U. S. Highway 2. This thirty-mile strip is unspoiled and beautiful mountain wilderness. Reaching down and across on all sides are deep incisions that erosion has cut into the body of this massive range. Cupped in cirques and in glacial valley depressions lie countless lakes, all strikingly lovely. Many of these could be visited by seaplane, but scenic geology can usually be best enjoyed on foot—for land forms should be approached slowly if their significance and history are to be more than a fleeting, soon-forgotten picture.

The southern Cascades of Washington, those extending from Snoqualmie Pass to the Columbia River, differ greatly from the northern ones. This part of the range is generally more subdued, though occasional peaks assume lofty elevations. Whereas a variety of rocks makes up the northern Cascades, chiefly two compose the southern portion—volcanic rocks and granitic material. The volcanics overlie the granitic. This condition is easily observed in the Tatoosh Range in Mount Rainier National Park.

The highest peaks in the Cascades are volcanoes formed by spectacular eruptions which are a part of the geologic history of this range. In some instances, however, irregularly-shaped peaks rise to exceptional heights. Yet they are not volcanic. Chief among them is Mount Stuart (elevation 9470 feet), a massive granitic peak in the Wenatchee Mountains—a spur of the Cascades—which extends southeast between the Yakima and Wenatchee Rivers. Some believe that Mount Stuart, with others of its kind, is a monadnock, that is, a rock remnant left standing as a result of extensive erosion all around it. Others contend that the Wenatchee Mountains were uplifted to a greater extent than other parts of the Cascade Range.

In Oregon, the Cascade Mountains represent both the old and new in mountain structures. On the east, the older Cascades parallel the Willamette Valley. These mountains show strong signs of having undergone many eons of erosion by the forces of nature. Such forces have weathered and scoured once higher elevations into the rounded lower Cascades of today. The geologist finds that the rocks in these ancient mountains are very complex. In general, Oligocene and Miocene flows make up much of the main body of the range. Tuffs, or solidified volcanic fragments, can also be found, as well as granitic intrusive core.

The High Cascades which flank the Western Cascades on the east are youthful in comparison with many of their neighbors. These took form in the Plio-Pleistocene when volcanic eruptions of liquid lava and ashes built a line of young volcanic peaks that eventually dwarfed the lower landscape around them. From these vigorous vents came new liquid rock which in some places poured out on the lower Western Cascades. The Three Sisters, standing in symmetrical alignment, are perhaps the best known mountains in the High Cascades. They are lofty, alpine peaks. Though they have been attacked by intensive glaciation, their imposing, snow-capped heights are visible far into eastern Oregon. The face of the High Cascades on the east is steep and, since this side shows a uniform alignment, the presence here of a fault in the structure is quite likely.

The Wallowas

The Wallowa Mountains in northeastern Oregon seem to have been set aside by nature as one of the monumental areas in the Pacific Northwest. In size and ruggedness they have the grandeur of the dark forests of Bavaria and the glacial scars of the Pleistocene (Photo No. 2). They form part of a mountainous region in Oregon extending northeast from the Deschutes Valley through the Blue Mountains and on up into Washington. Besides the Wallowas and the Blue Mountains, there are the Elkhorn, Greenhorn, Ochoco and Strawberry mountains. In fact, all of these mountains are sometimes included in the Blue Mountain group. Best known among this group are the Wallowas, which form a semicircular cluster about twenty-five miles in diameter, rising to nine thousand feet above sea level.

Historically, the Wallowas fit into the sequence of events of much of eastern Oregon. Coral fossils now attest that there was invasion by the sea. The remains of marine life became limestone, and shale and sandstone were formed. Igneous magma slowly cooled and was later uplifted. There were lava floods which added more weight for the rising land to lift. In fact, a weight-lifting battle marked the growing period of these picturesque mountains. They were forced to rise in a sea of lava which hindered uplift and which, in many instances, clung to the rising sides—or remained inside the structure—of the uplifted rock. All the mountains in the Blue group are

Photo No. 2   *Oregon State Highway Commission*

The Wallowa Mountain wilderness, with its sharply-eroded peaks and snow-flecked slopes, typifies much of the Pacific Northwest's scenic geology. Vantage point here is high on the moraine overlooking glaciated Wallowa Lake.

surrounded by lava or contain pockets of this rock. All are dissected by erosion, including the lava plateau which the mountains once fought for existence.

Glaciation modified and beautified the valleys. One glacier outdid all the rest by plowing a seventeen-mile trench from the summit of Eagle Cap down a river canyon, piling lateral moraines as high as seven hundred feet along its sides. Before it was through, its deposits had dammed the entire valley and formed an exotic setting for Wallowa Lake. The glacier still exists but, since it is only a few hundred feet long, its remaining life may be only a matter of years. The Wallowa Mountains lie in a region of contrast. Among them are peaks which tower nine thousand feet, while a few miles eastward lies Hell's Canyon, 3500 feet deep.

Two widely separated areas in the Pacific Northwest have much in common—the head countries of Wallowa Lake in northeastern Oregon, and Lake Chelan in north central Washington. Both lakes were created by valley glaciers; both reach back into unspoiled mountain wildernesses of snow-crowned peaks, alpine glaciers, rock-rimmed lakes, and sharp, eroded ridges. There is country in these areas which can be likened only to Austria or Switzerland— peaks on which only the most experienced should climb, but scenery which both the skilled climber and the amateur can enjoy (Photo No. 3).

The Okanogan Highlands

The Okanogan Highlands seem to hang across the Canadian border in northern Washington like a valance on a huge natural stage. Extending north and south between the Okanogan and Selkirk valleys, these rolling and often precipitous highlands

Photo No. 3   *Oregon State Highway Commission*

The head of Wallowa Lake, in northeastern Oregon, showing the formidable peaks
beyond, and the glaciated U-shaped valley filled, in part, by the lake.

appear in direct contrast with the Columbia Plateau which they meet on the south. The enveloping flow of the Columbia basalt stopped at the southern extremity of this upland region and may even have engulfed a part of it. The Columbia River is now the dividing line between the plateau basalt and the granitic highlands. When driving along the Columbia River—especially on U. S. Highway 97, along the north shore—portions of granite appear among the brown basalt seen across the river. This suggests that the spurs of granite may extend into and under the many flows. On the other hand, detached portions of basalt can be found on the highland side. This indicates the Columbia did not choose a course which followed exactly the dividing line of the two varieties of rock.

Gorge-like, north-south valleys slice this region into inter-highland areas. The Entiat and Methow valleys have several narrows, bordered by steep mountain walls. The Okanogan, which is wider, has many low-lying, rounded hills sloping down to the Okanogan River. These barren grass- and sage-covered mountain remnants once bore the great Okanogan ice lobe which originated in Arctic regions and crept southward beyond the Columbia River.

It is assumed that general folding originally accounted for the topography of the Okanogan Highlands but abundant intrusions, complex local uplift, and severe erosion have, to a large extent, obscured much of the structure of the region. Sediments in the form of limestone and conglomerate attest that this inland area was once under the sea. Whitestone, an elongated mountain near Tonasket, Washington, is an uplifted limestone mass over which the Okanogan glacier once flowed. Since then, intermittent streams have opened the sides of Whitestone, exposing a series of bedded layers and leaving some spire remnants which are excitingly scenic. Perhaps this contributes to the popularity of the region. Complex uplift also creates depressions in which water can collect. Many of the lakes are well stocked with trout. The higher, forested area in the highlands is the home of the largest mule deer herd in Washington.

The Okanogan Highlands represent an older section of the Pacific Northwest, much older than their neighbor, the Columbia Plateau. Some even believe that this highland was once a peneplain or flatland resulting from prolonged erosion, and that present erosion is at work on the again uplifted land. They point out that the streams of today follow fault lines or structural depressions.

Idaho's Mountains

Several areas in the Pacific Northwest can boast of mountain realms where man has not yet explored sufficiently to know the country well. Much mountain terrain in Idaho is virgin wilderness—still as new as the landscape seen by Lewis and Clark. The mountains are typical Rocky Mountain representatives, north of Yellowstone National Park. Their summits rise to a fairly level horizon but the ranges are not linear, a shape common among mountains. Rock which is uniformly resistant underlies the whole area. There is plenty of room for exploration in Idaho's mountains. The southern and western boundaries meet the Snake River and Columbia lava plains. The northern boundary is at Clark Fork on the Clark Fork River. Far to the east, the Idaho mountains are bounded by the foot of the Continental Divide.

The heterogeneous arrangement and puzzling structure of the mountains in this region give it an interesting physiographic history. Mountain areas have risen in the Pacific Northwest, only to be worn down before new mountains were again pushed upward. Such is the case in Idaho. Once a group of ancient mountains stood in this area, much like those of today, but they were eventually leveled by the never-ending process of erosion. Later, subterranean forces buckled the land and a new uplifted surface rose, on which rivers and streams again became incised. A new spectacular phenomenon then occurred, this time in the West. A flood of lava poured over thousands of square miles, and, in time, invaded the valleys of western Idaho, welling up against the mountain spurs. Rivers were dammed by the sticky, molten rock. Lakes appeared quite suddenly against the solidifying dams to provide a deposit place for the sediments brought downstream from the mountain heights.

As time went on, streams cut downward into the lava plateau. Long-undisturbed sediments were thus once more loosened and carried downstream. During glacial times, the higher elevations in Idaho were attacked by glaciation. Today hundreds of cirque-scars can be seen from the air or from ascent on foot to these elevations. The mountains of Idaho now represent the stage at which another peneplaining cycle began, in the misty eons of geologic time. Millions of years will be required to reduce these peaks to a plain, devoid of the beautiful mountain landscape of today.

As long as there are mountains, men will seek them out and climb them—if only to stand for a moment at the top of some rocky spire as the conqueror of the huge mass beneath. Climbing, though, is only one of the desires which mountains create in men. They are also historically interesting, even exciting. If the Pacific Northwest were merely a vast plain, there would probably be little incentive to investigate or to write about land forms. As it is, the Cascades, the Wallowas, the Blues, and all the rest beckon endlessly.

Chapter 3

AGES OF ICE

Glaciers interest nearly everyone, but few understand their origin or the work they perform. Tourists traveling through areas once occupied by glaciers—or those who see one of the few remaining glaciers—will enjoy the experience much more when they learn to recognize the land forms created by them and also how these earth sculptors operate. The Pacific Northwest bears many scars from their erosive action and, in some areas, ice remnants of them still exist. Large portions of the region contain earth features definitely linked with the invasion of ice from polar regions; some valleys in Alaska are still in the grip of the last ice age.

During the glacial periods, vast areas of the earth were covered by thick sheets of ice. It seems strange that so much ice could form then when no such phenomenon has visited the earth in historic time. Several theories are open.

It was once explained that the glacial age began when the earth assumed more of a tilt on its axis than the twenty-three and one half degrees which it dips away from vertical today. Such a change in northern areas would, of course, have caused the temperature to drop. This theory might work, allowing for an increase in moisture to make snow, which in turn would form the tremendous masses of ice. Still, what made the earth tilt? It is difficult to imagine a gravitational force, if such were the case, which could change the inclination of the earth, or, for that matter, cause it to resume its former position.

Another theory, and one which is widely accepted today, regards the fluctuations of solar energy as the cause of glaciation. It is known that the sun warms the earth at the rate of 1.94 calories per minute, per square centimeter. Although this is called a solar constant, it can hardly be classed as such because of variations which frequently occur. Observers have noticed that a slight variation in this constant reflects itself in prevailing weather.

Ice Age Weather

Primitive man may have lived near the southern fringe of the then-enlarged ice cap, but he left no weather records in the caves where he sought shelter. Busy with the job of securing food, he had little time for advancement in science, especially meteorology. Later written records, as well as the evidence found in earth deposits and plant growth, indicate that the earth has undergone dry, hot, cold, and wet cycles. Like the cold periods of the glacial age which lasted for many centuries, these cycles endured for great periods of time.

It is from these definitely-proved, short-period fluctuations that we must assume that longer cycles once occurred. There is convincing proof that long-time weather cycles have visited the earth. For instance, there is coal in the antarctic. To make coal, nature must grow large quantities of vegetation under warm conditions for long periods. According to those who study and record the weather of the earth, we are headed toward warmer and drier times. There is news of a diminishing water supply in some parts of the country. In several places the water table has sunk to such a depth that pumping is impossible. Most present glaciers are receding. Since events such as these are now facts in our weather record, it is safe to assume that different weather cycles likely visited the earth to shroud the northern latitudes in long spells of severe weather.

Both amateur and professional earth scientists are free to imagine the weather prevailing during glacial periods. There were certainly extended periods of dark, heavily-clouded skies, with temperatures low enough for snowfall. There were summers, or periods of melting, because water escaped from under the ice, carrying with it the sediments destined for deposit to the south. In contrast, long ages probably passed with the icy covering caught in bitter cold, unable to move or melt.

The record-breaking snowstorms of the Pleistocene Age, as the glacial period is called, surely required unusual amounts of snow-forming moisture. We know that this moisture came from the very same "cloud-factory" in operation today — the oceans. Geologists have found that during the Pleistocene Ice Age the level of the oceans was many feet lower than that of present shorelines. This suggests that great amounts of moisture were drawn from these oceans.

The surface of the globe on which we live has changed many times. Each geologic period, with its own epochs, experienced the destruction of old land forms and the construction of new ones. Results of these changing periods show in volcanic eruptions, sea inundations, earthquakes, stream and river deposits, and erosion by water, wind, and ice.

Of all geologic ages the most dramatic was the Pleistocene. A span of a million years encompassed the events of this period, the last of which are still fresh in the Pacific Northwest. During this time, ice once covered thirty-two per cent of the earth's surface. Cold times were separated by interglacial periods as warm, or warmer, than present climates. Ice dwindled and may have entirely disappeared. These events were repeated several times in the Pleistocene Age.

Ten per cent of the earth's present land surface is covered by ice, much of which is still in glacial form. In continental North America most glaciers are now found in the coast ranges of the Alaska-Yukon area. Greatest of these is Hubbard Glacier, seventy-five miles long. Smaller glaciers exist on the volcanic peaks in the Cascade Range of Washington and Oregon; and in the Olympic Mountains, west of Puget Sound. Glaciers in the Rocky Mountains are almost nonexistent. A few occur in the Lewis Range in Glacier National Park, and in the Wind and Teton ranges in western Wyoming.

Glacier Types

There are two types of glaciers. One is called continental because the ice in this type originated in north polar regions and spread outward to cover vast areas of our continent. Canada—from the arctic regions to its southern border—lay for centuries under blue ice. In the United States, all the northern border states were partially covered. Yet, with the exception of ice-covered Greenland and Antarctica, no continental glaciers exist today. In these two widely separated areas are the last remnants of continental ice invasion.

Valley glaciers, the second type, are the kind seen today, formed by the snows that accumulate on the higher mountains. They have their source at great altitudes in huge masses of ice packed into stream-cut ravines. Glaciers even exist at high elevations in the tropics. In the Himalaya, Mount Annapurna, 26,492 feet high, has several glaciers.

Objects located on a slope, especially those of great weight, tend to move to a lower level. Glaciers, both continental and valley, occupy slopes. The continental type, which covered the polar area and extended far to the south, rested on a portion of the sloping earth but the gradient was not steep enough to cause the ice to slide down. Movement of this type occurred when deposits of snow turned into viscous ice bulging sufficiently to make the outer rim creep farther and farther from the massive pile to the north. Having been formed on high mountains, valley glaciers are much more influenced by the gradient of the land.

A vast amount of ice is needed to advance continental glaciers. In some places the ice of the glacial age was more than five thousand feet thick. In other places it reached twice that. Powered by this great weight, glaciers are the earth's mightiest levelers, gougers, and depositors of rock, sand, and gravel. Their work puts to shame present-day, earth-moving machinery.

Continental glaciers probably caused the most severe type of erosion ever to visit the earth. Since this ice covered whole landscapes, nothing escaped. Mountains were rounded or planed to ground level. Rock underlying the soil was stripped clean, and now lies barren, deeply scratched by fragments of stone. River valleys which existed before the coming of the continental ice sheets were changed by the enveloping ice. Many large basins, now filled with water and used for transportation, were created by continental glaciers. The Great Lakes, whose waters carry ocean freight to the heart of a continent, were formed this way.

Valley glaciers confine themselves mostly to deepening their own channels. They trim off the ends of tributary ridges lying in the path of the all-powerful ice and round out the valley walls holding them on their course. Glacial valleys are always U-shaped and, when viewed from mountain highways or from the air, are examples of gracefully curving symmetry. High mountain lakes cupped in rocky amphitheaters are the beginning point of valley glaciers; they also mark the former presence of these glaciers. In glacial valleys one can observe the depth and width of the ice which once occupied these interesting troughs. In some of these, glaciers are still at work. Others are completely ice free.

Work of Glaciers

Glacier work is indicated by many signs, some unmistakable, some which must be interpreted by experts. Those which can be readily observed include the shape and contour of the land and the rounding and scratching of bedrock. Since glaciers are earth movers, they must make deposits when they can no longer transport their load. These earth deposits offer interesting exploration. Continental glaciers scraped off vast quantities of top soil, making the country of their passage almost useless to agriculture. Such an area exists in the Canadian Shield in northern Manitoba. Bedrock lies bare and the hollows have become countless lakes. Thus, by the action of a moving ice sheet, the geographical area of Canada has lost considerable "real estate," in the form of soil, to its southern neighbor, the United States.

The soil and gravel pushed forward by the edge of a continental glacier, and also by the end of a valley glacier, form terminal moraine. When the landscape enthusiast comes upon these unsorted piles of soil and gravel, he can be sure he has found a place where either a continental or valley glacier ended its work. Valley glaciers collect large quantities of debris against their sides because much rock is loosened by the scraping of the ice along valley walls. Some of this rolls and grinds between the ice and the valley trench. With the disappearance of the ice, this material lingers on as unsightly rubble, or lateral moraine.

A person wishing to explore a glaciated area should learn to recognize other deposits left by glaciers. In addition to moraine, another important deposit is till. This consists of tightly-compacted materials of many sizes and it is never layered. Pebbles, sand, clay, and large partly-rounded boulders make up its assortment. Since glaciers gather their loads from widely-separated areas, the pebbles and rocks may represent a variety of types. This rock may be partly angular, scratched, or even highly polished. A till deposit, examined in a residential section of Seattle, was blue clay containing small pebbles. It was so closely packed that a geologist's pick was needed to loosen the particles. This indicated that the great weight of the ice riding above it had acted as a huge compressor.

The underside of a glacier is not always level. It may dip into depressions where lakes form, or it may arch over obstructions. Long, oval hills formed under glaciers are known as "drumlins." These vary in length from less than a hundred feet to more than a mile. Since they are enlongated in the direction of movement, drumlins indicate the course taken by glaciers. The steeper end faces the direction from which it came. Generally this is north, or nearly so. If one were lost in an area where drumlins existed it would be fairly easy to determine the north-south direction.

Although scars from the most recent glacial periods are still fresh in the Pacific Northwest and some glaciers still exist here, glaciation is not a new phenomenon. In some of the earlier periods of which we have records, glaciers also left their marks. For instance, glacially - scratched conglomerate can be seen in the depths of a gold mine in Africa. Layers of rock representing millions of years of earth-time may rest above a stratum which was once surface rock beneath an ice sheet.

If there were no glaciers on earth—and no such ice had been present for a long time an explanation of certain glacial features would hinge solely on conjecture. Fortunately, however, glacial features can easily be understood because we can observe actual glaciers at work. In the Pacific Northwest, glaciers can be reached with very little effort and on countless mountain heights. Visiting them, one can observe their tremendous power and their fascinating features. For the sportsman, some glaciers provide excellent coasting and skiing even in the hot summer months.

Chapter 4

GLACIERS AND GLACIATION TODAY

A photographer flying high in the Alaskan sky over one of the surviving ice fields of the glacial age can capture with his camera the image of a dying glacier. Though still a giant, the glacier is now only a remnant compared with those which filled northern valleys at the peak of glacial times. The photographer's evidence helps interpret the Pacific Northwest landscape, which has no new glaciers but many remnants of ancient glaciers.

Maclaren Glacier

No large glaciers comparable to the size of those found in Alaska today exist in other parts of the Northwest. In Maclaren Glacier (Photo No. 4), located on the south side of the Alaska Range, portions of its exposed walls slope into a rounded, U-shaped valley, which is considered typical of glacial valleys. Lodged in basin-shaped hollows are the cirque snowfields which feed Maclaren, sending their ice downward to form the main glacier. Maclaren shows clearly how glaciers are fed and the shape of the places which nourish them.

The rounded crescent-like deposits far out in front of the ice tell the story of the dying glacier. These are terminal moraines consisting of ground-up rock which the glacier has pushed out of the trough in which it flows. The ice once extended to

Photo No. 4   *U. S. Geological Survey*

Maclaren Glacier on the south side of the Alaska Range in Alaska Note the medial moraines, the terminal moraine now free of ice, and the numerous cirques where former glaciers began their flow to lower levels.

the farthest edge of the circular area. Many lakes and potholes occupy depressions between the piles of deposited material. Several streams still carry water from the melting glacier. Thus a look at the present is also a look at the past, and, since we know how glacial valleys appear when the ice is gone, we may visualize how this valley will appear when the ice age, still present in this area, has finally ended.

Glacier National Park

Though Glacier National Park and Swiftcurrent Valley (Photo No. 5) do not have a still-active glacier as large as Maclaren, they do have certain similarities which show the work of a glacier and also the reason Swiftcurrent Valley became U-shaped. A rather long glacier left behind a fine

[35]

Photo No. 5   *U. S. Geological Survey*

U-shaped Swiftcurrent Valley, Glacier National Park, Montana. The glacier which
modified this valley moved eastward from the Continental Divide, leaving a rounded,
scoured valley bottom in which lakes now lie.

example of a glacial trough; also several features
commonly associated with valleys of this kind.

The glacier was supplied with ice produced by
heavy snowfall in Montana's Glacier National Park
Rockies. Ice flowed slowly east, down the gracefully-
curving valley and out upon the distant plain in eastern Montana, where the water moves toward the
Missouri and Mississippi rivers. The ice was deep.
Its under surface scraped everywhere on the valley
bottom, which is now covered with coniferous trees.
In three places, deeper gouging left ready-made beds
for lakes. Ice extended high up on the valley walls on
both sides. Grinnell Mountain, on the right, shows
glacial cutting almost to its top. Appekunny Mountain, on the left, was probably covered as far as the
vertical cliff on its side. Rock particles, loosened

from the mountain walls, have been rolling into the valley for centuries and these accumulations are now steep talus slopes reaching far up on the rocky walls.

Bedded in the area lies much banded rock, very old and sedimentary, deposited in a sea during bygone ages. There are hundreds of layers of water-deposited material. After the sea disappeared, these hardened materials were forced upward into towering mountains, a link in the majestic Rockies.

Erosion began from water running in mountain streams. Then the glacial age crept in, cold and silent. For a long time mighty blizzards piled deep snow in the mountains. This snow turned into ice for the glaciers which ground relentlessly in ever-deepening troughs. Ice flowed as a viscous mass out to a plain. When glacial times ended, beautiful Swiftcurrent Valley remained as a retreat for the vacationist and the lover of mountain flora.

The Rocky Mountains of Glacier Park seem to have experienced more than their share of buckling, faulting, and general earth distortion. The result is one of the most rugged areas in the Pacific Northwest, if not in the whole West (Photo No. 6). Glacier Park trails traverse sheer cliffs and follow sharp ridges where rugged wilderness is apparent at every turn.

Faulting here has been severe. That tremendous mass of rock, now called Chief Mountain, was pushed upward, then skidded eastward for eighteen miles. Much of the rock which accompanied the old "Chief" on his travels has since eroded; and this remnant, a sizable one even today, now stands alone at a 9066-foot elevation, northeast of a large family of peaks grouped together in this part of the park.

Photo No. 6   *Glacier National Park*

Lake Janet in Glacier National Park, Montana. Clearly exposed here are the buckling, faulting, and general earth distortion that characterize the Rockies in this area. Note the bedded nature of the rock.

The great uplift and general shifting of massive blocks of sediments, which once lay undisturbed in the sea, provided the pressure necessary to change, or metamorphose, the original rock in these Rockies. Thus shale became argillite; sandstone lost its granular character and became quartzite; limestone, a true product of the sea, through pressure and combination with magnesium carbonate, became the very hard dolomite. Operators of diamond drills— using the hardest cutting tool known—frequently have trouble cutting through dolomite.

The processes of mountain building seem to have ended at Glacier National Park. Man has found this rugged area to his liking, so much so that he has set it aside to be "unimpaired for the enjoyment of future generations" as well as his own. He has of course named the region Glacier Park because of the sixty glaciers which still exist there. A highway across the park is called "Going to the Sun." This runs along the precipitous rock walls marking the approach to the continental divide at Logan Pass, 6664 feet above sea level. Lakes, streams, waterfalls, fields of alpine flowers, forests of evergreen trees, dozens of mountain peaks—all make this a land of enchantment high on the backbone of the Rockies.

Two peaks of this region especially stand out. Mount Cleveland at the northern edge of the park is the highest, with an elevation of 10,448 feet. Triple Divide Peak, in the south central part on the continental divide, with an elevation of 8001 feet, is the most unusual. Down its sides drain waters destined for three distant seas. The water from the melting snow on the north side of this peak finds its way into the Arctic Ocean, while down the east and west slopes flows water which in time finds the Gulf of Mexico and the Pacific Ocean.

Mission Range

There are some land forms in the Pacific Northwest which stamp indelible pictures in the memories of those who have seen them. One of these is the Mission Range, in a sense an extension of the monumental mountain structures of Glacier National Park, but set apart from them as a smaller member of the Rocky Mountains in western Montana. Mission Range is seventy miles long and occupies a north-south trend, south and east of Flathead Lake. A magnificent view of the range appears at Ronan and continues to the east, if you travel north on U. S. Highway 93. The steep, rugged walls of the west side of this range rise abruptly from the green flat on the Flathead Valley. The panorama one sees from Ronan includes glacial cirques, which now hold everlasting snow; and pyramid-like peaks with grim, dark walls of barren rock and serrated ridges, notched and broken by the weathering of time. This is mountain grandeur—a part of Montana at its best.

The Mission Range has one characteristic of much interest to the person who delights in reviewing the record of the glacial age. The northern end of the Missions slopes markedly to the north. At first one sees nothing unusual about this, but the interesting fact about the subdued character of the range here is that it has been planed down by glacial scour. The uplifted rock was unable to divide the advancing ice effectively. As a result, ice crept up the northern end of the Missions, carrying away great quantities of rock. Interpreting glacial geology can be a fascinating part of enjoying the Pacific Northwest.

Steens Mountain

Steens Mountain, extending almost north and south for nearly a hundred miles in southeastern Oregon, houses Kiger Gorge, a glacial valley as near U-shaped as can be found anywhere. Its curving valley walls are so well proportioned that, when photographed, they seem to have been laid out by a draftsman (Photo No. 7). Steens—the highest mountain in southeastern Oregon—was the only place in the region visited by glaciation.

This mountain, standing alone on an extensive plain, has other features which interest both geologists and tourists. It has been folded and faulted so intensively that great blocks of it have been tilted and seemingly torn apart, leaving almost perpendicular walls down which the climber can look five thousand feet to the bottom of the great rifts.

Steens Mountain is composed of two igneous flows, both more than four thousand feet thick. The older flow is known as the Steens Mountain series and consists of gray-to-black volcanic rock and poorly-layered flows. The younger flow, which lies atop the Steens series, is basalt. This basalt, which extends over the entire length of the mountain, differs from most of the basalt seen in Oregon and Washington. In it are elongated, flat crystals about an inch in length with numerous openings between them. Steens Mountain formations can be seen clearly from the Alvord Ranch on the edge of the Alvord Desert. Although Steens Mountain is located in an arid region, its highest portions have been severely dissected by both water runoff and glaciation. Water for erosion has come to this area because of its altitude. The cooler temperature condenses moisture borne by the atmosphere.

Photo No. 7   *Oregon State Highway Commission*

Kiger Gorge in Steens Mountain country is the only example of glaciation in south-eastern Oregon. Viewed here from Rim Rock, far above the floor of its U-shaped valley, it shows classic symmetry in glacial carving. Notice the hanging valley at the upper right.

Kiger Gorge, a striking example of the work of valley glaciation, is not the only place where ice has been at work on Steens Mountain. Nearly all the streams which flow eastward off the Steens begin in glacial cirques. The upper Blitzen and Indian Creek valleys are glacially U-shaped; and Fish Lake, at the head of Fish Creek, owes its existence to a glacier which worked out a depression for it.

Cascade Glaciation

The abnormal snowfall of the glacial epoch covered the northern Washington Cascades with a deep

[42]

mantle of snow which gradually compacted into ice as the Pleistocene storms continued. In time, alpine glaciers formed in the high divide area and flowed east and west down already eroded valleys. Although extensive glaciation visited the east side of the Cascades, even greater volumes of ice occupied the western valleys. This was true because, then as now, more precipitation from the ocean was captured by the western slopes.

Among the eastward-flowing glaciers were those which occupied the Stehekin, Methow, Yakima, Icicle, Wenatchee, and Similkameen valleys. Each of these had branches of ice fed by main glaciers which operated independently in adjacent depressions. Two of the largest eastern Washington glaciers were the Similkameen-Okanogan and the Chelan. The Similkameen-Okanogan pushed down these valleys with power generated by ice far in the Canadian North. The Okanogan ended its work after crossing the Columbia River. The Chelan extended from the Cascade divide for seventy-five miles to the canyon in which flowed the Columbia River.

The Columbia River was the boundary beyond which Cascade and Okanogan Highland glaciers rarely passed. True, some basalt masses, plucked out of the plateau rim, are found south of the river, but these have not been carried far. The Wenatchee glacier flowed out of the Cascades into the Columbia as far as Rock Island, about six miles below Wenatchee. There is a high terrace, north of the valley below Wenatchee, which may be a large outwash deposit from the Columbia River ice mass. Another terrace, 1400 feet high, east of Wenatchee, could have been formed as a lateral moraine.

Chelan Glacier, which released great quantities of gravel into the Columbia, is responsible for many of the downstream deposits in this area. It is believed that the 850-foot valley train terraces near Wenatchee were formed out of material from this glacier. Many miles of the Columbia are strewn with sand and gravel loosened by glaciers and carried downstream by the swift water.

Western Cascade glaciers flowed out of vast groups of connecting ice fields. During the peak of glacial activity, ice and snow covered many of the lower hills on the western Cascade slopes. The glaciers emanating from this tremendous ice field were thicker and wider than those which plowed down the eastern Cascade side. Most important of the west slope glaciers were the Sauk, Skagit, Skykomish and Snoqualmie.

Fortunately for the traveler in the northern Cascades, most glaciated valleys now have highways which follow the surface once occupied by grinding ice. Here can be seen such features as rounded valley bottoms, deposits of unsorted gravel, truncated spurs, and at times glacial striations.

Glacier-Carved Puget Sound

Some residents of the Puget Sound area wryly tell tourists that in the very early days a certain Peter Puget was hired to dig Puget Sound. He was an energetic excavator and took pride in neatness as well as efficiency. To avoid cluttering up the landscape, he put all the dirt from this large basin in one huge pile, which was later named Mount Rainier. Then came Paul Bunyan who contested Peter's contract. Nothing much came of the argument except that Peter, in a rage, began throwing dirt back into Puget Sound, thus building the San Juan Islands.

Actually Puget Sound appears to be the largest glacier-carved basin in the West. So deep is the water in this ice-cut basin that battleships can tie up at Seattle docks, and the channel into Sound ports is wide and deep. The tourist in the Puget Sound country will find himself traveling on long strips of land jutting out into the Sound. These are separated by equally long fingers of water.

Twice in the Pleistocene Age, and probably earlier, thick lobes of ice crept slowly down from British Columbia fields, entering an already existing structural depression in the Puget Sound area. These lobes were enlarged by still more ice from north Canadian caps. Not just local tongues of ice crawling down a mountain valley to die on plains a few miles from a mountain cirque—these were the "main show," the western edge of the massive sheet which capped the entire top of our planet and extended far to the south.

Many geologists have examined the country where the glaciers left their loads of debris before a warming climate stopped them. Bit by bit they have studied the marks left by ice on adjacent mountains. They have studied the lakes left in gouged-out hollows, and the sediment carried down rivers at the southern extremity of the ice. Thus the story of the glaciers—their size, depth, and performance—has been put together.

These facts are part of the story: Ice extended from the Cascades to the Olympic Mountains, even pushing itself up into some of the lower valleys of these highlands. Drift, or unsorted glacially-carried materials, has been found sixteen hundred feet above sea level on Mount Rainier and a distance of approximately eighty miles up the Dosewallips River on the south side of the Olympic Mountains.

The ice extended almost to the sites now occupied by the towns of Tenino and Centralia. South of the farthest advance of the ice lobe are piles of moraine arranged in the usual mounds of glacially-deposited material. Varying with the topography of the country on which they rest, moraine materials range from 150 to 1400 feet above sea level. In the Chehalis River Valley, southwest of the moraine belt, are extensive areas clogged with sand and gravel deposited by the outwash from the glacier, which used the Chehalis River as an outlet to the Pacific. There are also many low-lying mounds about which geologists have pondered ever since they first began studying the Puget Sound country. These mounds may be seen near Cedarville on State Highway No. 9.

Moraine deposits on both sides of Puget Sound in the latitude of Seattle indicate the ice was four thousand feet thick. Ice is a heavy substance, weighing 57.2 pounds per cubic foot, so millions upon millions of tons of sheer weight were driven into the Puget Sound area. It is no wonder that a basin into which an arm of the sea could enter was scooped out of the earth by a force such as this.

Study of a topographic map will disclose that the water of Puget Sound has drowned an extensive drainage system. At an earlier time, as at present, several rivers and streams flowed from the higher land—which borders the Puget Sound trough—into an enlongated depression, through which they cut channels that forked or branched and then reunited. Water, collecting in this basin, drained northwest to the sea through the Strait of Juan de Fuca. The system was then modified and in part completely erased by the Puget Sound Glacier. Many of these channels or "canals" still remain, though they are now different from what they were in former times. Some of them have become filled with silt, especially in upstream areas. The Puyallup Valley, southeast of

Tacoma, is almost completely filled. The Duwamish, another silt-receiving channel, has filling yet to be completed, nearer the Sound. Some of the depressions in the trough are occupied by lakes. Lakes Washington and Sammamish, east of Seattle, are the largest and best known. Their basins follow the same pattern as other erosion channels in the Puget Sound country.

It is a mellow land, the Puget Sound country of today. Its mild marine climate produces forests and dense undergrowth that are almost tropical, yet it is part of a natural wonderland that has been excavated between two great mountain ranges.

Lake Chelan—Valley Glacier

Lake Chelan in north central Washington is a fine example of a lake made by a valley glacier. There are two clues to prove its glacial origin. First, the mountain walls which hold the melted snow water of the Cascades are curved everywhere along its course to bottom level, and they are typically U-shaped. The contour of the valley alone would strongly suggest that a glacier had been at work here but there is a second and better piece of evidence. In order to hold water, glacial valleys must be dammed by a moraine, an accumulation of earth and stone. The glacier which gave up its work at what is now the town of Chelan, on U. S. Highway 97, pushed an excellent fill across the end of the valley. For a time this moraine held the melt water of the glacial age in this vicinity at a much higher level than the lake has today. This level is preserved high above the town in several terraces which look as though they had been cut by ancient waves.

The dam left by the glacier was not durable, judged by present engineering standards. In prehistoric days the overflow water of the lake removed much of the gravel and silt of the original barrier. It worked its way down to bedrock in a steep gorge so that Lake Chelan water tumbled into the Columbia River, three miles from the outlet. Now at this site there is a concrete and steel dam to control the level of the lake, assuring a continuous flow of water through its power-producing turbines.

The trough which once held the Chelan Glacier begins in the heart of the Cascades and winds southeastward for about eighty-five miles to the terminal moraine, three miles from the Columbia. Fifty-five miles of this route is occupied by Lake Chelan, which in one place is fourteen hundred feet deep—three hundred feet below sea level. The depth of this excavation makes the Lake Chelan trough one of the outstanding glacial canyons of the West.

Tributary valleys in the upper lake area also held glaciers, but, since the master valley contained more ice and was therefore a more energetic digger, the tributary valleys are not so deep. They are classed as "hanging valleys" because their mouths lie some distance up on the main valley walls.

One of these heads in a magnificent rock-rimmed amphitheater known as Horseshoe Basin, an immense rock-rimmed cirque down which water falls in countless ribbons of spume. On these walls grow moss and lichens that weave a tapestry of vivid color. Here began the journey of much of the ice which made up the Chelan Glacier, and in this region fell the snow which kept it alive. Searching for Horseshoe Basin is a thrilling outdoor adventure. Though an unimproved mine road penetrates the area, it is more enjoyable to walk at least a part of the way. For a short time the route follows the Stehekin River as it rushes toward Lake Chelan.

On the way to Horseshoe Basin are three or four farms, probably begun by homesteaders, but long since deserted. Their log cabins have fallen in ruins. It is said that a few hardy souls came here in 1900 to farm this wilderness but were soon conquered by the deep winter snow, the dense growth of trees and brush, and the utter isolation—no roads lead to the settlement.

It is interesting to conjecture what would have happened if the Chelan Glacier had continued another three miles before it was forced to stop. Its trough would have joined the valley of the Columbia; then this river, for a time, would have been dammed, either by moraine or by ice. If the present outlet had been lowered to approximate the level of the Columbia there would have been no Lake Chelan. Instead, the Stehekin River would now flow from the Cascade Mountain Divide to the Columbia.

Recently some discoveries in the terminal moraine area near Chelan have furnished new information about glacial history here. Three erratics cause speculation about some of the glacial events which occurred between Chelan and the Columbia River. One of the erratics lies near the Chelan Hospital; one is found along the Chelan-Manson road, which follows the lake shore; and the third is buried in lateral moraine some distance above the town on the Chelan-Butte road. All of them are basalt and all lie from four to six miles from the nearest basalt deposit on the east side of the Columbia River. The only apparent way for them to have been loosened from the northern edge of the Columbia Plateau and carried upward into the Chelan Valley was by glacial ice.

Columbia River Glacier

A glacier in the Columbia River? Yes, the signs are there. Eighteen miles upstream, where the Methow River enters at Pateros, large erratic boulders are strewn from the mouth of this river along the right bank of the Columbia for a distance of about a mile. They have come from Methow Valley where glacial evidence is plentiful. Between the Methow and Lake Chelan valleys the tributary spurs have been cut off. Near Azwell, U. S. Highway 97 passes a well-formed kettle, some distance above the river. It is hard to believe that a glacier would turn abruptly from its course in the river and travel upward for about 450 feet to push into a tributary valley—yet the erratics which a glacier carried are surely there.

At this point come into play some interesting conjectures. One must ask: Did the river glacier enter after the Lake Chelan ice had receded? Did both glaciers meet head-on at the end of what is now Lake Chelan? Should we discard the idea that these were carried here by a glacier and substitute the theory that—at the close of the ice age—they were rafted in by floating bergs on a tremendously swollen river which carried flood water from a large ice-packed area? A seemingly ordinary boulder, half buried in sand and gravel, can indeed be the key to new vistas in the realm of geology.

No highway has been built to the head of Lake Chelan. On the west side it is possible to drive to Twenty-Five Mile Creek, which is the distance from Chelan. Much of this road has been blasted out of nearly perpendicular rock walls. To see the changing panorama of the entire length of the lake, it is advisable to take passage on the motor launch which

Photo No. 8   *Washington State Advertising Commission*

Lake Chelan in north central Washington is a glacially-created lake, extending into the Cascade Mountains for fifty miles, with towering peaks flanking its shoreline. Part of this lake is below sea level.

makes daily trips from Chelan to Stehekin. You can breakfast in Chelan, lunch in the rustic inn at the head of the lake, and be back in Chelan in time for dinner.

Photo No.9   *Washington State Advertising Commission*

The rocky shoreline of Lake Chelan here shows the scouring of glacial ice. The sloping, hilly land in right center is moraine material of glacier-rounded soil and gravel. Apple orchards today thrive in this deposit.

Cruising on the blue water of Lake Chelan is a delightful experience. A camera should be handy to use on the mountain goats, deer, and occasional bears which can be seen on the steep walls that plunge into the lake. Pine and fir trees and flowering bushes clothe the mountainsides. The changing bluish tints of the lake—caused by different intensities of the light entering the lake canyon—and the imposing Cascades make each bend in the lake an unforgettable picture (Photos Nos. 8 and 9). Like the Catskill Mountains described by Washington Irving, the Cascades act as a weather barometer for the people of Chelan.

Glacial Lake Missoula

Glaciers are the best scratch-makers of all. They pay no respect to the valleys in which they travel, scarring everything they touch with their sharp, icy sides. It is strange how ice, almost frictionless, can cut the grooves on steep rock walls (Photo No. 10). Actually the huge lobe of ice which crept into the valley came well equipped to do a good job of scratching. Frozen solidly into its great volume and held securely by the pressure of hundreds of feet of ice, this huge mass carried rocks of various sizes which it had pried loose along its route. Some of these rocks had sharp edges, capable of cutting into any surface over which they passed. Probably no modern factory has cutting machinery powered with a force even approaching the power of a valley glacier, armed with claws of stone.

Like the small boy who cuts, then repents, and tries to erase his mischief, the glacier did almost that. Not all the original grooves remained when the ice melted because the ice also contained much fine material, some as fine as powder. This acted as a polishing agent. The smooth areas on the wall were left by these fine grains of sand which smoothed over the coarser cutting of the boulders that had gone ahead.

Glacial scratches, called striations, are found on the first roadside cliff of any size after leaving Clark Fork, Idaho, going east on U. S. Highway 10A. These glacial marks often lead to interesting discoveries, such as those near Clark Fork. They tell a story which leads into western Montana and shows

Photo No. 10

Glacial striations along U. S. Highway 10A, near Clark Fork, Idaho. The Glacial scratches point out the direction of the glacier which dammed the Clark Fork Valley, creating ancient Lake Missoula.

the relation between these striations and a unique feature of glacial time.

These striations occur on the north wall of the Clark Fork River Valley, a short distance from the river mouth on the east side of Lake Pend Oreille, in northern Idaho. The Clark Fork rises in the Rockies near Butte, Montana, and flows westward in a

Photo No. 11   *Idaho Department of Highways*

Coeur d'Alene Lake in northern Idaho occupies a basin scooped out by a tongue of ice in the Pleistocene Period, a time of extensive glaciation in the Pacific Northwest.

deep valley throughout its course, flanked on each side by high mountains and deep tributary valleys.

In glacial times, northern Idaho was invaded by a tongue of ice that, retreating, left hollows in which Priest, Pend Oreille, and Coeur d'Alene lakes now lie (Photo No. 11). The scratches on the walls indicate that ice from the north Idaho lobe entered the Clark Fork Valley, closing its outlet. This valley is not U-shaped; it has more of a faulted appearance. Since it does not have a rounded valley floor, we can assume that it was not glaciated. The ice therefore

[55]

entered this valley only a short distance and then only temporarily.

With the closing of the outlet of the Clark Fork. something unusual must have happened. Evidence of how the Clark Fork reacted to this is not found at its lower end but, instead, 160 miles to the east around Missoula, Montana, where wave-cut beach lines appear hundreds of feet above the valley floor. These indicate that the Clark Fork Valley had filled with water, resulting in ancient Lake Missoula, one of the largest bodies of water ever to collect in western United States. Montana University students have laid rocks together to form an "M" on the side of Mount Jumbo, directly behind their campus. This "M" can be seen from the streets of Missoula; near it is a series of parallel beach lines representing stages in the life of Lake Missoula. Beach lines appear several places west of Missoula, around Arlee and Hot Springs in Sanders County. Beaches were cut in the eastern end of the lake because here, at high elevations, the rounded hills are covered with soil. At the western end the mountains are chiefly rock with only slight amounts of soil.

Glacial time was not one of continuous freezing. There were intervals when ice and snow thawed, causing melt water to flow from under glaciers and ice fields into valley basins and streams and rivers. In the closing years of this age, however, there was more thawing than freezing. Ice in great volume and thickness still remained, but its power waned as warmth crept over the land. With ice movement at a standstill, the force of running water became dominant. During this period of prodigious ice melt, erosion of the land increased enormously. Scars from these cutting waters are still evident.

The runoff time was a period of destruction and also of deposition. Could man have viewed the great Pleistocene Lake Missoula he would have seen yellow, muddied outwash, creeping up the sides of the Cabinet and Coeur d'Alene Mountains, until a thousand feet of water lay above the silt-filled bottom. In a later century, men interested in learning the depth of sediments in this ancient lake drilled into them a few miles east of Paradise, Montana, where they found three hundred feet of silt and blue clay. At this depth, they stopped drilling, not knowing where bedrock might be.

Water from ice in the nearby Flathead Valley and snowfields of the North poured into the gigantic basin of the Clark Fork. Judging from the large amount of silt in Clark Fork Valley, large delta deposits could be expected at the mouths of its north wall tributaries. Surprisingly only a few exist. Best known of these is the Vermilion delta at the mouth of Vermilion Creek in the western end of the valley. The top of this delta is 320 feet above the valley floor, proving that the delta was formed when Lake Missoula stood at that level. The Vermilion delta gained prominent size because the valley mouth, where it rests, extends northward through a low pass which connects with a tributary of the Kootenai Valley to the north.

In the Lake Missoula period, a glacier occupied Kootenai Valley. Water and sediments from the Kootenai spilled over the low divide between it and the Clark Fork, building the delta in the partly-filled Clark Fork. Had natural conditions been different at this time—such as deeper water in Lake Missoula and deposition of sediments at a higher lake elevation by Vermilion Creek—Clark Fork Valley might have been completely dammed by better material than the ice which made Lake Missoula only a temporary feature. If this had occurred, a lake might still exist there.

There came a day when glacial ice in northern Idaho weakened. The ice dam, which perhaps persisted longer than is suspected, crumbled in the warmth of the new era. What happened next has probably never been duplicated. Finding the valley once more open, the millions of acre-feet of impounded water in Lake Missoula moved westward in the most tremendous flood of the closing days of the Pleistocene Period. Gravel, silt, and millions of tons of deposited material in the bottom of the lake were torn loose and flung along in a maelstrom of churning water. Tributary mountain valleys acted like riffle boards in a sluice box. As the torrent of gravel went by, these served as catch basins for immense amounts of material plucked from the valley walls (Photo No. 12).

Thinking that surely these deposits must have been the work of tributary streams, the writer climbed to the top of one of these gravel dumps, then up the ravine at its back—but found no evidence of a stream ever having occupied the valley. These numerous deposits are not stream deltas. They were lifted there in a torrent of water, rock, and mud in the drainage of the prehistoric lake from the sudden rupture of its temporary dam. Motorists traveling along U. S. Highway 10A through Clark Fork Valley can observe these unique features.

Nearly everyone has noticed the washboard-like surface of the sandy bottoms of streams — or of the land that water has temporarily passed over. When bottom materials are rolled along, smaller particles travel faster than coarser pieces. Depressions at right angles to the current are thus devel-

Photo No. 12

Gravel deposits appearing in the V-shaped area are decidedly out of place in this tributary gulch of the Clark Fork Valley in Montana. Several such deposits were sluiced from the turbulent water of Lake Missoula, which flowed westward with the rupture of the glacial dam during the closing days of the Pleistocene period.

oped between the faster and the slower moving particles. These undulations on stream bottoms are called ripple marks. In sand having medium-sized particles, the distance from crest to crest varies from three-fourths of an inch to two inches.

Many Montanans do not realize that their state has ripple marks of a size probably surpassing any in the world. A number of these eye-catching forms are at least a hundred feet from crest to crest, some extending even farther, whereas most ripple marks are only inches apart. A good place to see these mammoth marks of ancient Lake Missoula—and to take pictures—is on State Highway 28, between Plains and Hot Springs. A short walk east along the northern boundary of Clark Fork Valley leads to a fine vantage spot.

These marks add more evidence to the rapid departure of water in Lake Missoula, when its icy dam failed at the western end. They lie on a grassy slope where present-day cattlemen range their herds and hope that sufficient rain will fall to assure plenty of grass. A few thousand years ago there was no vegetation here. The ripple-marked slope was a water-soaked, muddy grade which had just been violently disturbed by water escaping from one of the most remarkable lakes in the strange glacial age.

There is still more evidence of this sudden outpouring of water. Gravel from Clark Fork Valley is strewn over wide areas across northern Idaho as far as Spokane Valley. Because of the high gravel content of the soil, gardening is a losing venture in some sections of this outwash area.

The outwash area does not end in Spokane Valley. Beginning at Cheney and continuing westward for about seventy miles, then southwest to the Columbia River, is an area which the eminent geologist, J. Harlan Bretz, calls "the scablands of eastern Washington."

The area is appropriately named. Although a considerable portion of this swath of land is farmed —that is, the pockets of good soil which lie widely scattered in the scablands—the largest part is a jumbled area of basalt islands or mesa-like formations, separated by a network of channels. These channels have one identifying pattern; they are roughly parallel, with a northeast-southwest trend. They contain water-worn gravel, stream-bars, and potholes, such as would be found in any active stream today. However, except for small lakes and ponds filled by springs or by snow melt, they are all dry. Few streams now erode these channels yet each bears characteristics of water erosion.

The failure of the ice dam at the western end of Lake Missoula occurred in the warming period which marked the decline and end of the frigid Pleistocene. The huge quantity of water that poured from the Clark Fork Valley surely reached the area now classed as scabland and in all probabilities contributed mightily to its erosion. No land surface could long resist such a flow, because this was a violent flood, armed with sharp gravel and traveling rapidly.

Lake Missoula was not the only source of water in this changing period. North of the scabland area lay tongues of ice, rapidly melting and pouring water south. Much of this certainly found its way to the scabland channels.

Thousands of motorists have passed the cliff on which the glacial striations may be clearly identified. Countless others have visited Missoula, where the beach lines appear high above the city. Those who have learned the story of Lake Missoula know that even scratches on a valley wall are clues to ancient times.

Skykomish Valley Lake

Another glacier-created lake once occupied the lower end of Skykomish Valley in Washington, but clues which point to this impoundment differ greatly from those which led to the discovery of Lake Missoula. Unlike Clark Fork Valley, the Skykomish Valley is U-shaped and at its mouth is piled moraine pushed down by the descending ice. When this glacier with its moraine reached the mouth of Skykomish Valley, its movement was checked by the massive Puget Sound Glacier, which blocked this valley entrance as well as others opening into the Puget Sound basin. Here, for a time, the two bodies of ice remained unchanged, with the moraine material, gathered in the Cascades, squeezed between the two glaciers. When the ice age ended, the valley glacier must have melted first, as evidence in the form of thickly-bedded clays, upstream from the moraine dam, indicates that a lake once occupied the lower end of Skykomish Valley.

The moraine here, as in other places, proved inadequate. Skykomish River washed over its earth dam, completely removing the moraine from one side of the valley. The river did a real service in making this opening, for through it now run the Great Northern Railroad and U. S. Highway 2. Both of these cross the Cascades—the railroad through an eight-mile tunnel at Scenic, Washington; and the highway over Stevens Pass.

Photo No. 13   U. S. Geological Survey

Glacial cirques in the Rocky Mountains of Colorado. Plucking action of ice, which moved down these troughs, removed rock from the rounded amphitheaters in the high ridge country, making them appear like gigantic bear tracks.

"Bear Tracks"

Daniel Boone, flying over the Colorado Rockies, would no doubt have looked down in awe at the round depressions in Photo No. 13. Far below him he would have seen what appeared to be mammoth bear tracks, the largest he or any other hunter of his day had ever beheld. The earth looks as though it had been raked by mighty claws, and the marks of what seem to be footpads are visible in some of the amphitheaters. Three are clearly shown, and a fourth appears in the distance. They suggest that a huge primeval bear once tramped down this ridge.

These depressions are called cirques, the starting points of local glaciers. The bowls in the mountains are the areas where the heavy accumulation of snow, packed in the headwaters of mountain streams, turned to glacial ice. When the weight of the ice reached the point where it could no longer remain stable, the ice started downhill. A glacier was thus born on the slopes of the Rockies. As more ice formed at the head of the glacier, additional rock was plucked from the mountain and carried downward; and as the cycle of ice formation and movement was repeated, the cirque deepened.

Just below the sharp peak at the upper right of the photograph is another cirque, the starting point of a new glacier, this one longer than those on the lower ridge. This glacier traveled down between the two sharp ridges which begin at the head of the valley.

None of the glaciers in the region is very long because all were forced to join a glacier occupying the large valley, through which the highway passes today. In glacial times this valley was more U-shaped than now; and, since the glacier disappeared, streams have cut quite deeply into the valley floor.

Cirques occur whenever mountains are high enough to support glaciers. In the Pacific Northwest these include a profusion of peaks, beginning in the Rocky Mountains and ending where the moist winds scatter snow on the peaks fringing the Pacific Ocean. All Pacific Northwest cirques once fed glaciers and some are the source of ice and snow for still-active glaciers. Because all of the region's volcanoes have at one time been attacked by alpine glaciation and some even now bear active glaciers, numerous cirques are visible on all of them. The spire-like peaks in Glacier National Park, the Northern Cascades in Washington, the Olympic Mountains, the High Cascades in Oregon, and the mountains of Central Idaho—all have semicircular basins scooped out by the destructive plucking of alpine ice.

Erratics

At several locations in the Pacific Northwest, large boulders, for no apparent reason, rest on top of the land surface. Such a boulder is shown in Photograph No. 14. This barren, sage-dotted slope is typical of many arid localities in the West. The scene becomes more interesting on noticing that a large boulder on the horizon is decidedly out of place. It is a foreigner, so to speak, because rocks of this size are not often found on the surface of the earth far from outcroppings of similar materials. The area in which this stranger rests is composed of deep sand and gravel, several miles from any other rock. Why then is this rock mass in such a peculiar environment?

The rock extends about twelve feet above the ground (Photo No. 15). It is granite and has one crack near the top that caught some windblown soil in which brush now grows. Since granite can be found in the distant mountains, this specimen may have come from there, or from farther away. As this region was once overrun by a broad valley glacier, the explanation for that lone rock probably lies in the happenings of glacial times. Glaciers, entrenched in valleys, caught the debris which rolled down the valley walls.

Suppose that this large rock was once a part of a cliff overlooking a broad expanse of ice creeping slowly down the valley below. Water could have penetrated the cracks which separated the rock from the parent granite. Then, when cold weather came, the water would have turned to ice. Frozen

Photo No. 14 *above:* Distant view of the glacial erratic in Okanogan County, Washington. Note that the rock rests alone in an area devoid of rock, suggesting transportation from its place of origin.

Photo No. 15 *below:* Close view of the erratic seen above. Note the rounded appearance, caused by friction from its travels and subsequent weathering. This erratic may have come from the mountains seen in the distance.

water expands, and, though it may not seem possible, large rocks are actually moved when a considerable amount of water in the crevices around them freezes. This boulder was no doubt freed in such a manner. Suddenly it rumbled down the valley slope, the roar echoing in the icy air. Down the hill it sped to meet the ice lying in wait to receive it. Its final resting place was now to be decided by the power of the moving ice. How long the ice carried its burden it is hard to say. When the ice melted would have been the time the boulder settled into the soft earth to become a lonely landmark for the cattlemen of today.

Boulders of this kind are known as glacial erratics, another strange glacial product. The one shown in Photo 15 is located in the Havillah country of Okanogan Valley in Washington, a short distance off U. S. Highway 97. Basalt erratics appear near Waterville, Washington, and in the vicinity of Coulee Dam on the Columbia River. These were plucked from the edge of the Columbia Basalt Plateau in glacial times and carried some distance by the ice when, at scattered places, it crossed the Columbia River. Locally these large, rounded basalt masses are called "haystacks." In the Puget Sound trough, erratics are common. Those at Tenino, for instance, are found 650 feet above sea level.

Willamette Valley Erratics

Hundreds of boulder erratics and thousands of smaller erratic fragments have been discovered in the Willamette Valley in northwestern Oregon. Erratic Rock State Park was built at the site of the largest erratic so far found here. It is slate and is located between McMinnville and Sheridan. Although erratics lie scattered over a wide area in the glaciated part of the Pacific Northwest, it is surprising to find them in the Willamette. This valley was not glaciated and, what is more important, the mountains surrounding it are composed of rock different from that of the erratics. The geologic processes which transported the boulders to this foreign environment are a fascinating phenomenon.

The northern Cascade Mountains, the Olympic Mountains of western Washington, and the Coast Range of British Columbia and southern Alaska, all contain the granites, quartzites, and gneiss, of which the erratics of the Willamette Valley are largely composed. All of these mountain areas are scoured by glaciers which, in some places, reached the Pacific Ocean. Icebergs, containing rock from these regions, were no doubt set adrift when the ice was freed from the mountain valleys. However, for berg-floated rock to reach the Willamette from these sources, ice would have to float down the Pacific Coast, into and up the Columbia, then turn south into the Willamette, and in some way negotiate the valley gaps at Lake Oswego and Oregon City. Such a journey seems highly improbable.

Better evidence in similar erratics is found along the middle reaches of the Columbia River and its tributaries. Boulders, often of considerable size, strewn along the course of the river could have come only from the upper part of the Columbia River basin and been rafted by large chunks of ice or river-bergs which had broken loose from melting glaciers to the north. Then they could have floated down the Columbia in the swirling water at the close of the Pleistocene Age. As glacial lakes were drained, huge quantities of water were periodically released into the Columbia. This took place over a long period of time, the tremendous quantities of melt water producing floods in the Columbia far greater than those of historic time.

Nowadays debris in a flooding river must be cleared from stoppage points to prevent impoundment of water and further flooding. In the Pleistocene Age it is entirely possible that the lower Columbia became clogged with ice and that, for a time, temporary dams collected water that flooded into tributary valleys. The low-lying Willamette was thus easily flooded and into it floated the rock-laden bergs. Erratics, encased in the melting bergs, dropped to the bottom as the ice dissipated. It is also easily conceivable that, during short-period stoppages of the Columbia, bergs in the Willamette settled to the bottom with the receding water. In either case, the rock brought from far upstream had finally become erratic. Ice-rafting would seem to be the only way to explain the interesting boulders in the Willamette Valley.

River Terraces

In Photograph No. 16, a touchdown is in the making but — to the trained eye — the background landscape is just as exciting. The terrace, formed against a mountain of rock, offers interesting speculation.

Little grading had been necessary to level that football field. The terrace extends in both directions. Behind it appears another terrace and above it a third, but less pronounced. This third terrace is composed of gravel and sand covered by a thin mantle of soil. And beyond all this is rock. How were the terraces built? Where did all the gravel come from? What force brought this material to rest against the mountain of rock?

Coleman Crowe

Photo No. 16 *above:* Terrace formation, Okanogan County, Washington. Note the even elevation of the top of the terrace and the glacially scoured rock on the hill beyond the terrace.

Photo No. 17 *below:* View of the same north Washington valley on the side opposite the football field, showing its corresponding tiers of terraces. These terraces represent various stages in the disappearance of the valley glacier. The lower one has been badly cut by gully erosion.

A clue stands out as sharply as the referee's shirt. Look again at the mountain. The rock is exposed in long, rounded forms, as if something had smoothed all of its uneven features. So little soil is present that trees are widely scattered and seem to be struggling to grow. These signs point to a glacier as the primary designer. Since this area is in the northern part of the Okanogan Valley in Washington, where valley glaciers scoured the land, glacial evidence is conclusive. The subdued mountain in the background is typical of those which stood in the path of the glaciers.

If a glacier caused the terraces in this area, tracing their origin becomes an interesting geologic problem. Part of the rock waste was probably shoved along and below and at the sides of the glacier. A vast amount of it also would have been carried in the flood water running southward when the glacier melted. Millions of tons of this fine material were likely swept into the abnormal runoff that swirled down the valley and around the hills remaining in the broad valley. Much of it lodged along the sides of the waning glacier. Finally, when the ice subsided, the terraces built on its sides remained.

If one side of the valley had been filled to an even depth, then the opposite side would also have terraces, and these should correspond approximately in elevation with the football gridiron and also with those elevations behind the field. They do. The lower terrace corresponds very well with the football field terrace. And above it lie well-defined second and third terraces, representing various stages in the disappearance of the valley glacier. Beyond these terraces was the same kind of glaciated mountain with identical features. The lower terrace on that side of the valley has been badly cut by gully erosion (Photo No. 17).

The terraces described here are part of a series which would rank high in extent and in quantity of material with any group of terraces in the world. They lie in the Okanogan Valley of Washington, which extends from the Canadian border to Brewster, where the Okanogan empties into the Columbia. Along the entire valley, a distance of seventy miles, gravel and silt terraces slope away from every mile of the river. Because of the symmetry of these treeless bench-like forms, this valley offers both pleasing scenery and geologic interest. U. S. Highway 97 runs along the various terrace levels in its route through the valley.

Since the bottom of the Okanogan Valley is now obscured by the deposits of glacial time, the traveler may wonder how deep this valley was cut before it became clogged with glacial sand and gravel, and also how great the volume of melt-water was which tumbled these particles into place when the ice retreated north. Journeys on Pacific Northwest highways are far more provocative for those who can build yesterday's land forms from today's characteristics.

Kettles

One of the most symmetrical land features left behind by glaciers is the kettle, sometimes so perfectly rounded, with gracefully sloping sides, as to appear to be man made. Some contain water where springs drain into them or where the water table happens to be higher than the kettle bottom. Photograph No. 18 shows the shape of a kettle. Here a farmer is using a spring-fed one for irrigation

Photo No. 18

A glacial kettle in Okanogan County, Washington—one of the many to be seen in glaciated valleys of the Pacific Northwest. This one, almost a perfect circular depression, is spring fed and rigged for irrigation.

water. His sprinklers can be seen in operation on a field of alfalfa.

This kettle is found in the Aeneas Valley, a tributary of the Okanogan Valley, in Washington. There are well-shaped kettles between Azwell and Chelan, on U. S. Highway 97, and many south of Puget Sound.

Glaciers plow their way down valleys or across continental areas regardless of what lies beneath the ice. Soft earth, such as sand and gravel, will often yield to large masses of ice which gouge great depressions under the glacier. When a glacier is in full movement these depressions are only temporary. The ice moves on and the hole, occupied for a time by the ice, is modified or destroyed. Kettles are formed during the last movements of a dying glacier. The ice which has buried itself in the ground is now unable to move. As it melts, water swirls around the earth-lodged ice. The result is a rounded kettle.

Mount Rainier has many glaciers, some still clogging upper valleys with ice. Since the lower parts of these glacial troughs can no longer sustain ice, their characteristics are easily examined. Some Mount Rainier valleys extend to the Puget Sound lowlands, where roads and highways make access to them easy. The Nisqually, Tahoma, Puyallup and Carbon are among those whose mouths lie at the edge of this area.

A drive up Hurricane Ridge into Olympic National Park, from Port Angeles, offers many splendid views of glacial valleys. At the summit of the ridge appears a panorama of mountain splendor with active glaciers showing in the distant Bailey Range. From this scenic ridge you can look down into several ice-carved valleys sloping to the low-lying Strait of Juan de Fuca.

All of the glaciers which encircle Mount Hood can be seen from the highway which leads around this mountain. There is the view from Horseshoe Bend, for instance. Here one can see the "neve"—compacted granular snow of the upper end of the glacier—still occupying the crater, whose sharp rim is struggling for survival against powerful ice erosion. At a somewhat lower elevation, sharp ridge remnants protrude from the ice, remnants of a much more extensive mountain. Cirques also can be seen feeding small glaciers. There is no better place for observing glaciers in the whole Pacific Northwest.

Beautiful Crater Lake in Crater Lake National Park, Oregon, occupies the caldera of ancient Mazama. Now devoid of glaciers but scarred by them in the long ago, its outer slopes bear cirques and radial glacial lines, proof that in the days of its youth its peak was crowned with ice and snow. Whereas Mount Hood can be circled at its base, old Mazama has a road entirely around the famous blue lake cupped in its volcanic crater. According to Lewis A. McArthur in "Oregon Geographic Names," "Crater Lake is one of nature's marvels. It is more in the nature of a scenic wonder than anything else the writer has ever seen. Oddly enough it is not a real crater at all, because it occupies a caldera far larger than the crater of the original mountain."

Chapter 5

THE UNDERGROUND WATERS

Underground water is an essential part of man's environment. Its presence in a particular region sustains the population which otherwise would have to depend on piped water, or live elsewhere. Water probably travels as extensively underground as on the surface, accounting for the diffused settlement pattern of the earth's inhabitants. The Pacific Northwest has an abundance of this subterranean water. Some of it, under pressure, spouts into the air; and some of it—through the chemical action of water and heat—splashes the region's landscape with pastel tints.

Water underground is a kind of mechanic. It may erode and enlarge earth tunnels through which it travels; it may do mischief by wetting rock or clay, down which sections of earth can slide and damage home sites. Land creep from hidden waters can be detected by cracks in hillside ground and the lowering of portions of ground along them.

Geysers

Perhaps no feature of the landscape attracts more people than a geyser in action. In Yellowstone National Park, for instance, summer tourists wait patiently for Old Faithful to perform. Watches are consulted, cameras are readied, and late-comers run from hurriedly parked automobiles.

Suddenly the pressure which has built up underground finds expression. There is a rumble of rushing water. Then the air is filled with the roar of ascending water and steam. Old Faithful rises in a white plume, higher than the surrounding forest. Water bursts through its rocky throat until it seems that the earth around it might break. Explosions from the expanding steam send out constant smoke-like jets (Photo No. 19).

The display ends when the expended water splatters to the ground and no more water belches from the earth. Water vapor is the only indication that, a few minutes earlier, thousands of gallons of hot water were spewed into the air. Tourists go about their sight-seeing—commenting as they walk in such manner as this,

"It sure takes a lot of water to run these 'geezers,' but I suppose they turn them off during the winter months."

Geysers are rare compared with better-known natural phenomena. Perhaps that is why their operation is not generally understood. Early-day trapper John Colter is reported to have fled into what is now Yellowstone Park when the Indians threatened his life. There he was safe because the Indians regarded this area and its thundering geysers as the abode of demons. Hiding among his protective geysers, Colter probably could not have explained what made them spout and steam, but nowadays there is an explanation for these "volcanoes" of water. In fact, they are duplicated in laboratories.

It is well known that the interior of the earth still contains much heat, enough to melt rock. Heated rock must lie beneath a geyser area. Next, water must be introduced. Underground veins of water with a constant flow feed into deep levels through

Photo No. 19

Lone Star Geyser, Yellowstone National Park. The layered cone of silica, deposited by the erupting water, is plainly visible.

joints and cracks until they reach the heated area. This is the beginning of geyser eruption. Water heats to the boiling point on the hot rock. As more and more adds its weight, pressure is increased and with it the boiling point. Still more water, still more pressure, still higher temperatures. When the water above can no longer hold down the steam and boiling water below—then the geyser performs. Steam and water rush upward through the cracks and tubes which, before eruption pressure was reached, carried the water downward.

Old Faithful, one of the most famous geysers in the world, averages sixty-five minutes between eruptions. It is noted for its regularity. Giantess, another Yellowstone geyser, erupts only twice a year, but it takes more than four hours to blow out its accumulated water and steam— and this to a height of two hundred feet. Old Faithful releases its pressure in a matter of minutes.

Hot water dissolves the minerals it meets along the tubes through which it flows. These minerals are brought to the surface with each eruption and are deposited as the water fallen to the ground around the vent evaporates. Delicately-colored designs resembling castles, turrets, and mounds form in places where geysers roar and spout.

Silica, dissolved underground and brought to the surface by erupting water, gives shades of gray and yellow to the designs that take shape around geyser vents. Algae, a group of water plants, often add their distinctive coloring. This versatile family of plants, with some members living even in snow, has relatives which like the opposite. More than a hundred kinds of algae have been found thriving and multiplying in water with a temperature of 187 degrees Fahrenheit. Except for a few species, hot water algae are usually blue-green. This color, mingled with that of silica, splashes a geyser area with soft, memorable pastels.

Though some geysers have ceased to erupt and new ones have burst into life during the time scientists have observed them, it is believed that generally they perform for a long time. In a very simple test, the yearly deposit of silica on geyser cones or outlets has been compared with the total thickness of some cones. This comparison reveals that thousands of years would be required to build the deposits around the outlets of certain geysers.

When it can no longer generate pressure in its arteries, the geyser's showy existence ceases. Internal complications, such as the diversion of its water supply or the cooling of deep-seated rock, cause a geyser to stop erupting. Later it often becomes a hot spring, a pool of hot water, or boiling "mud springs." These mud springs, which resemble boiling mush, are often associated with dying geyser activity. The appropriately-named Paint Pots of Yellowstone National Park occur in a geyser area and are doubtless remnants of once-active geysers.

Oregon has a most accommodating geyser. This one was drilled by an enterprising man, who, searching for water, unexpectedly created an unusual specimen—it erupts continuously. This unique spectacle can be seen at Lakeview on U. S. Highway 395 (Photo No. 20). The water which spouts high into the air must be connected with an underground heating system providing constant pressure. Lakeview Geyser is both scenic and practical. Its spewing, splashing waters, so enjoyed by sightseers, are also piped for indoor bathing and heating.

Water is many things. It is a constant wanderer, destroyer, builder, and worker. Landscape observers

Photo No. 20   *Oregon State Highway Commission*

Geyser at Lakeview in south central Oregon, from which water spouts continuously.
Unlike Yellowstone geysers, this one has no cone, indicating that the water at Lakeview
contains no cone-forming minerals. Water from the geyser has formed two small lakes
where Canadian geese rest during migration.

see its work everywhere. Without water, erosion would be left to heat, cold, and wind.

The amount of water in and on the earth, and in the clouds above it, is thought to be unchanging. When water vapor, born of the sea, is swept landward by the wind and chilled by the cool masses against which it strikes—rain is formed. It is true that many localities have about the same amount of rainfall from year to year, yet, over long periods of time, the rainfall which seems constant may vary considerably. Examples of extremes in wetness and dryness are common. In the tropics there are places where rain falls every day; whereas, in the heart of the Sahara Desert, up to seven years have passed without rainfall.

Rain water divides as it falls to the earth. Some of it becomes runoff, which finds its way into streams and rivers, at last returning to the ocean. Some rainwater seeps into the earth through porous soil, cracks in rock formations, mine openings, and holes dug by animals and insects. Portions of this water may sink several miles into the earth. There it becomes difficult to observe, and, when needed, often difficult to find.

Ground water usually appears at rather shallow depths, most of it collecting above a nonporous material such as clay or rock. The layer of water above this barrier is called the saturation zone; and the top of the water level, the water table. A lake surface is often a visible water table, and the water level of a well almost always is. Many river surfaces coincide with the water table.

There is no way of knowing how much water remains permanently underground but the amount is likely small. Sooner or later most of it reappears. Man digs wells into the water table to supply even large cities. Trees and other plants draw up ground water, then return it to the air by transpiration through their leaves. On a clear day a medium-sized elm can take several tons of water from the ground. Sometimes water reaches the surface through the same openings down which it disappeared as rain. Where air penetrates, evaporation can also take place. Thus, when it rains, water descends into the ground; when the sun shines and the earth is warmed, water vapor ascends into the air.

Springs

A spring is a surface outlet for underground water, controlled by gravity or underground pressure. From prehistoric time, man has always been closely associated with springs. In his earliest wanderings he traveled from one to the other slaking his thirst. The game he killed for food also used the springs. Occasionally blood has been spilled over the right to the waters of springs. With its absorbed minerals, this water is often prized for medicinal purposes; medicinal spas are popular among many who seek relief from pain.

Springs of minor scenic appeal gush from hundreds of outlets in the Pacific Northwest. They are important in providing water for cattle and for homes, and their presence has often determined the location of farm homes, even of towns.

A few springs, however, because of their size, mineral content, or variations in temperature, stand apart as unusual and interesting attractions. One of these is Lava Hot Springs, located at the town of the same name, in southern Idaho. Ranked by some as unique throughout the world, these springs occur along the Portneuf River where great volumes of therapeutic water pour out of the earth's interior.

Indians once enjoyed their health-restoring value, considering them as a gift from the Great Spirit. And, they set this place aside to be used by friend and enemy alike.

Some of the springs that were prized by early settlers provided only a trickle of water that had to be used sparingly. Lava Hot Springs pour out 6,711,-000 gallons of water daily—each spring having a different kind of mineral. The average mineral content of these waters is 962 parts per million. It is believed that this is the highest mineral content of any spring on the North American continent or in Europe.

One of the pools at Lava Hot Springs—Mud Bath —refuses to reach an overall temperature. Mud Bath swimmers encounter both hot and cold water, and varying temperatures in between. This is caused by the thirty separate springs which pour into this pool, all of different temperature.

Oregon Caves

There is always the possibility that caves may contain human clues to ages past. Though few caves in the Pacific Northwest have yielded records of ancient people, there is persistent hope that such vestiges will turn up. Their dark interiors, even their inaccessibility, stir the imagination.

Oregon Caves — sometimes called the Marble Halls of Oregon—were created by the solvent action of water deep within a mountain in the Siskiyou Range. History has it that this towering limestone and marble formation was discovered in 1874. In that year, dogs belonging to Elijah J. Davidson's hunting party bagged a bear and Davidson investigated the cavern into which the bear had escaped. This cavern became Oregon Caves (Photo No. 21). Since their discovery, a million or more people have walked

Photo No. 21   Oregon State Highway Commission

Joaquin Miller's Chapel in the Oregon Caves is typical of the underground beauty of
stalagmites and stalactites to be found in these caves. A partly fluted stalactite
appears in right center. Dissolved minerals redeposited on the cave floor create a
snowdrift effect.

through this wonderland maze of tunnels and chambers with their fantastic formations. According to the "Oregon Guide," "There is Niagara Falls, a waterfall frozen eternally into marble. Joaquin Miller's chapel . . . a vast cathedral-like room, named for the poet . . . Deeper within the mountain . . . Paradise Lost, a high-vaulted chamber from which hang the pendants of crystal chandeliers . . . Dante's Inferno . . . a yawning chasm in which marble, under crimson lights, resembles the contents of a boiling cauldron."

[85]

Nature followed the usual pattern in making the Oregon Caves. First, the great preparer, the sea, occupied southern Oregon. In time, shells of sea animals became limestone. Then the sea withdrew, leaving its deposits of lime to mark the basin in which it had lain. Then came uplift and, with it, great pressure on the layers of limestone. Under pressure, the limestone became marble. But the caves were still not ready for casual tourists. The water had yet to percolate into the lime deposit, dissolving large cavities and marking the dark interior with fantastic artistry.

A trip into the Oregon Caves is a journey into a million yesterdays. Incredible periods of time were consumed by dripping water to dissolve the marble rooms and build the beautiful formations of the floor, ceilings and walls. Today the many magnificent chambers are lighted with electricity—among them, Ghost Chamber, Dragon's Mouth, Paradise Lost, and the Chapel.

A journey into this silent wonderland reveals gleaming layers of marble, lapped like flows of sugar frosting; and fluted stalactites, some large, some small. Stalagmites reach up from the floor, occasionally joining similar forms from above to become shining pillars. Rows of stalagmites form the bannisters of stairways leading up to or down to pillar-filled rooms, and they support arches of grotesque beauty.

Time is important in the construction of stalactites and their counterparts. Evidence points to incredible slowness in the building of these delicate forms. Many hours, even days, may be required for a drop of water to collect on a cave ceiling. A few drops may deposit only a microscopic amount of mineral. Deposition is interrupted during periods of drought when, in some regions, little or no water finds its way into the ground. Of course in regions with a constant and copious supply of underground water, stalactites and stalagmites form more rapidly.

Ice Caves

Where the underground temperatures are low enough, water in subterranean openings often freezes. Should the accumulated ice remain in underground chambers the year around, these are known as ice caves. Three ice caves may be reached from U. S. Highway 97 in Oregon. Arnold Ice Cave is located fifteen miles southeast of Bend, South Ice Cave is fifty-three miles southeast of Bend, and Surveyors Ice Cave is about ten miles south of Newberry Crater. All of these have ice-coated walls, frozen formations caused by dripping water, or partly ice-paved floors.

Deep lava flows often create caves among their unique structures and, since much lava has spread over the land here, ice caves are a part of the interesting geology of Idaho. Shoshone Ice Cave, a huge cavern, is located under a lava field, fifteen miles north of Shoshone. Its huge chambers measure up to six hundred feet long and ninety feet wide. Its ceilings and walls hold a canopy of ice which reflects the torchlight guiding the cave explorer. Because its inner end is plugged with ice, this cave's full length will perhaps never be known.

To see a frozen underground river, visit Crystal Falls Cave, twenty-eight miles northwest of St. Anthony, Idaho. The principal chamber holds a frozen river, extending most of its length. This cave is a veritable fantasy land in ice. Everywhere in its dark interior are picturesque ice formations that resemble familiar and interesting shapes and forms.

Another cave of this kind, known as Ice Cave, is located near Paris, in the southeast section of the state. This small cavern is only eighteen by forty feet, yet is well supplied with ice throughout the year.

Other Caves

Idaho has a variety of caves. Kuna Cave, south of Kuna, is different in that air moves through it with noticeable velocity. Hot Cave, south of Twin Falls, is so hot that it has been only partly explored. However, six rooms have so far been discovered. At one time this cave contained flowing hot water but, since artesian wells were drilled nearby, the water in the caves has stopped flowing. Clay Cave, three miles north of Hansen, Idaho, is so named because the constant drip of water from the roof keeps the clay floor in a sticky condition. It is several city blocks in length, with many intricate, connecting chambers.

Another of Idaho's unusual caves is Wind Cave, near the town of Milner. Here the wind whistles constantly through numerous vents and, what is rarer, the air blows alternately in and out of the cave.

Formation Cave—also called Limestone because of its composition—is a few miles northeast of Soda Springs. It is narrow but extends three hundred yards into this sea-formed rock. The ceiling is decorated with delicate water-percolated designs remindful of lace or small plants.

Although Minnetonka Cave in St. Charles Canyon is mostly unexplored, it promises to be the most extensive cave in the state of Idaho. It is located at an elevation of 7500 feet. Perhaps the reason for its yet largely unknown character lies in its rugged chambers. However, Minnetonka Cave will not remain unexplored for long; each year new chambers are entered. This cave may prove to contain subterranean marvels which will make it one of the major underground galleries in the Pacific Northwest.

Idaho has some other caves which are known about but are largely unexplored. One of them is in Danskin Canyon on the South Fork of the Boise River; another is in the Salmon Forest at the head of Warm Springs Creek; and a third is fifteen miles south of Boise. That this third cave was once inhabited by primitive people is evidenced by the many artifacts of flint and other kinds of stone found there. Also, the ceiling is blackened by the smoke of long-dead fires.

Nature's Buttons

Underground water sometimes makes oddly-shaped objects when working on dissolvable material. The button-like rocks which appear on the side of the road-cut in Photo No. 22 are called concretions. These examples of concretion happen to be roughly disk-shaped, like the one upturned in the top right-hand corner, but their shape is not always uniform.

This spot, located on U. S. Highway 10A, a few miles west of Noxon, Montana, was once solid rock consisting chiefly of limestone. As in all rock structures, open seams probably allowed rain water and melted snow to percolate downward. Since limestone dissolves readily, sizable openings gradually develop from the water flowing through the cracks. The cementing process begins when mineral-charged water finds a fossil leaf, shell, or rock particle lodged in a water-made pocket. The foreign objects

Photo No. 22

The large button-like rocks are concretions found along U. S. Highway 10A, near Noxon, Montana. Being harder than the limestone in which they were formed, these interesting formations remained exposed as the softer rock disintegrated. When broken open, they showed well-formed prints of trilobites—small, prehistoric marine animals.

become the center of new masses of rock which grow in size as long as water is able to dissolve the limestone about them. Inside the rock mass, the concretions grow hard and round while the limestone crumbles and decays.

The concretions here exposed are of black chert, a very hard material. This writer spent part of an afternoon breaking up several of them in search of fossils. The reward was finding a well-formed print of a trilobite, a small bug-like animal now extinct, that scientists say was one of the first forms of life. Here, then, more than three hundred miles from the Pacific Ocean, once rolled an inland sea in which swam the trilobites now encased in rocky tombs. A bulldozer opening a passage for a modern highway had exposed these tiny, prehistoric bugs — and brought word of ancient waters on that land.

Chapter 6

NATURE - THE KEEPER OF RECORDS

Nature has been keeping records ever since the cooling earth formed its rocky outer shell. The innumerable changes from that time on are conceivably recorded somewhere on the vast expanse of our amazing globe. One reason many of these changes remain unknown is that telltale layers of earth are often missing. These gaps in materials, which should chronologically appear in some areas, suggest that key layers were worked out by cycles of erosion that scattered the materials far and wide.

Rock does not hold the only key to prehistory, though it does preserve the prints, charred remains, and the petrified bits of plant life of bygone ages. Within some rocks rest the bones of long-extinct animals, the story of their environment, their food, and how they died. In later periods, man's early writing and printing still exist on enduring stone. Beneath the soil, the volcanic ash, and the gravel wash, anthropologists have discovered the skeletal remains of prehistoric man.

Time is dramatic in all sciences, but especially in geology. To study land forms is to study the master work of time. Geologists face the enigma of layer upon layer of sedimentary and other kinds of rock. How long has it lain in its present position? When did the animal live whose fossil bones were found imbedded in its layers? When did the distant volcano build its graceful cone? How long did the glaciers last?

Geologists have learned that mountains or large land masses have risen and then been eroded to allow ocean flooding at intervals. Using this discovery as a measuring stick, they have divided earth time according to the occurrence of uplift and submergence. Periods of mountain building they call eras, and each era represents many millions of years. Subdivisions of eras they call periods—or the times of local disturbance. A period begins with the approach of submergence; it ends when the uplifted land has again been drained of the sea. An epoch is a division of a period. By separating time in this way, geologists can more clearly catalog the order of earth's happenings.

Many may think it futile to be concerned with geologic time, for the millions of years about which geologists speak and write cannot even be comprehended. Yet most of us like to connect dates with the natural events which we ourselves have experienced. We remember the spring flood of 1948, the unusually cold winter of 1950. There are people living today who are still telling their children and grandchildren about the great San Francisco earthquake. They remember what they were doing when it happened.

Although nature alters the land surface with incredible slowness, there are some changes which can be observed in a human lifetime. This writer as a boy fished in a lake that is a grass-filled marsh today. In the southern, dried-up end of Goose Lake, south of Lakeview, Oregon, the ruts of a wagon road are apparent. Immigrants of the 1840's had crossed there. The lake then filled, only to be shallowed again to reveal the road. Rivers often cut channels in a single freshet. Land slips or slides can overnight necessitate the relocation of roads and trails. In today's world, many of these changes are engineered by man, with his building of dams and his irrigation projects.

A geologic period—bounded by submergence and drainage—can be summed up as the culmination of all local disturbances which have been at work to accomplish a major land design. These periods become more fascinating with study. In them were formed the continents, the oceans, the land forms, the minerals, which, in a large measure, set the pattern for today's world.

A reader interested in scenic geology would likely not be concerned with a long account of all the geologic periods. Here, therefore, they are used only as aids in describing dramatic geologic events which created the physiographic wonderland of the Pacific Northwest. This landscape is the result of millions of years of building and destruction; of explosions, arctic cold and tropic heat. For the first time since life on this earth began, nature now has man to interpret and enjoy it—and the present is a fascinating period. Many scientists believe that never before has the earth's crust been so beautifully arranged, with its contrasting plains and snow-covered mountains, its rolling countryside, its deserts and rushing streams, its placid rivers and its turbulent oceans.

Two Islands in Oregon

It is interesting to fit a specific area into this vast amount of earth time—to account for as much of it as available information will allow. Portions of Washington and Oregon—including the land west of the Cascade Mountains and a strip east of them as well—have an amazing geologic story.

Such stories seem to begin in the sea; and the story of much of Oregon and Washington has such a beginning. Out in the depths of the sea — amid violent upthrust, intense heat, and earthquakes, heralding the arching of the sea bottom—land in the Paleozoic Era struggled to rise above water. When these savage forces subsided, two widely separated pieces of sea bottom had become land forms, islands in a still present sea. One of these, in the Blue Mountains area and possibly extending into Idaho, Thomas Condon named Shoshone. The other, now the southwest corner of Oregon and including a part of what is currently northern California, he named Siskiyou.

Men were not present to verify that these islands were formed in this manner, yet the history is there. First, fossils found in both areas are the same. On their perimeters, fossils of shells—sea organisms—have been discovered. From their location around Siskiyou and Shoshone it is easy to deduct that these organisms were found on former beaches. Furthermore, from the slate, marble and limestone occurring in this general area we know that the region between the islands was all of marine origin. Through the study of fossils and sedimentary rock, their relation to the sea and similarity in structure, we know that for a long period of time similar conditions existed over a large area, beginning in the Paleozoic and lasting into the Triassic and Jurassic of the Mesozoic Era, and continuing even into the Cretaceous period in later Mesozoic time.

Then the scene shifted. Again uplift came to disturb the sea between the islands. Slowly but surely great changes once more rearranged the shape of the land. All the disturbing forces which together accomplish uplift and create new land bodies, once more cracked and upfolded the bottom of the sea. The rock and hardened mud which finally took their place above the sea became the Cascade and Sierra Nevada Range—separating Siskiyou and Shoshone islands.

Millions of years passed. The Eocene period saw a shallow sea west of the Cascades, on the side where older Siskiyou still stood. Great quantities of sand —in which chambered shells are excellently preserved—were poured into this water. The result was Eocene sandstone, now lying exposed from Denmark, Oregon, north of Cape Blanco, almost to the mouth of the Coquille River. This rock appears again south of the entrance to Coos Bay; also from the mouth of the Umpqua River, upstream to Scottsburg. There are even Eocene fossil beds near Albany.

Like Shoshone and Siskiyou, the Olympic Mountains of Washington once stood offshore, an ocean island. During Eocene time these imposing mountains rose as giant sentinels, often obscured by the fog and storms from the Pacific Ocean. East of the Olympics, extending to the newly-formed yet lowlying Cascade Mountains, was a broad area occupied by many plant-choked swamps. Some of these fingerlike bayous reached into the Cascades, where their dense vegetation was destined to become the layers of coal mines of today.

Then, almost a hundred miles west of the Cascades, came the birth of the Coast Range, by the same subterranean forces which had created the Cascades. In the beginning of the Miocene period this range was only a chain of islands of uplifted Eocene rock, between which the tides of the Pacific rose and fell. Once formed, however, they made a long trough between the Cascades and the coastline mountains, extending from California far to the north in Alaska. The Willamette Valley in Oregon, the broad Puget Sound trough, and the San Joaquin and Sacramento valleys in California—all lie in this enlongated depression between these two mountain barriers. One of these, the Puget Sound trough, was later to be invaded by polar glacial ice, extending down the coastal trough into the Sound area.

This, then, is the brief story of the land west of the Cascades, influenced by warm, wet winds of the Pacific and the encroachment of ocean water, before mountain barriers sealed the water's entrance to this intermountain trough.

But what of the land of Shoshone? What excluded it from the west, behind a mountain barrier? For a time, the eastern lands remained much the same, as the Cascades were not yet high enough to capture the moisture from the west. However, the rising Cascades trapped considerable water lying east of them, making eastern Oregon a lake country in which western clouds and rain provided a favorable climate for plants and animals—both of which flourished during this time in the John Day country.

But the rising young Cascades did not provide a pleasant environment for the land to the east. Immense sheets of lava pouring out of ruptures in the earth changed the contour of this land. Falling ashes from several volcanoes filled the lakes and other earth depressions. When the Cascades finally reached their maximum height, the life-giving moisture—heretofore supplied by the western winds—could no longer reach eastern Oregon. A new climate had arrived, and it was dry. Hot summers and cold winters replaced the temperate marine climate of the coast.

With the advent of these harsh conditions it is little wonder that both life and the appearance of the land were greatly changed. Moisture-loving plants and animals declined. Lakes, filled with ashes and other sediments, dried up. Verdant foliage gave way to drought-resistant shrubs and grasses. Referring to this change in the John Day country, Condon comments in his "Two Islands," "True today it lacks the palm tree on the shore and the rhinoceros near its waters—but their graves are here, monuments that speak eloquently of other times."

Nature has a way of adapting life to the reverses of environment. The revolutionary changes at the close of the Cretaceous period brought notable alterations in the kinds of animal life. Early species were replaced by new ones. Reptiles — which had been the dominant vertebrate life of the Cretaceous —declined at the close of this period while mammals flourished.

Throughout the ages, these events have been enacted again and again. Never quite the same from one age to another, the shifting surfaces of the globe have seen old lands destroyed, then replaced by new ones which in turn caused changes in the kinds of life on them. The Pacific Northwest has a rich store of material available for those who wish to study this ancient, shifting landscape.

Pages From the Past

Time's changes are usually more apparent in land forms composed of thinly-bedded layers. The neatly-bedded formation in Photograph No. 23 is really a pile of stony sheets or plates flaking away to expose the layers below. This formation was not always rock—-it was once mud, gathered by streams in faraway mountains, then deposited in an inland sea.

Photo No. 23

Thinly bedded Belt-time sediments in Sanders County, western Montana. Once the bottom of an inland sea, these bedded layers reveal the extent of the submergence and the character of their deposits—which were made in one of the earliest periods known to man.

When the sea withdrew and the land once more rose, this mud hardened into shale. That was millions of years ago, for the pictured rock belongs to the Belt system of Pre-Cambrian strata. This means that the material which finally turned into rock was deposited in one of the earliest periods known to man—and his knowledge is limited to the earth layers which can be seen or be explored by drilling.

The sediments of Belt time, named for the Belt Mountains in Montana, were brought to an inland sea, estimated to have been almost three hundred miles wide and reaching from Missoula westward. Belt rocks have one distinction: they compose the greatest deposit of undisturbed rock in the world. Their symmetrical layers are much the same today as when they were arched up from the sea in which they were formed. The layers of mud became very deep, some of the mass now exposed ranging from twelve to forty thousand feet thick. The pictured example of Belt sediments was found in western Montana on what is known as the "cutoff," a road connecting St. Regis, on U. S. Highway 10, and Paradise, on U. S. Highway 10A.

These slabs are pages from the past. Assuming that the climate in Belt time had seasonal rains and snow, warmth and dryness, then each layer would represent the seasonal amount of soil that the rivers brought into the sea. Every slab in the picture, however, does not represent a season as we know it, for each slab shows its own faint lines of separation into other, thinner layers. With patience, thousands of seasons can be counted in one layer formation alone.

If life were present in the Beltian sea it had to be simple indeed. There are fossil reefs of a form of algae which may have lived in Belt time at Kootenai Falls on U. S. Highway 2, eleven miles west of Libby,

Montana. These contain tubular casts resembling the tunnels left by worms. Whether they were made by worms or by roots of some plant life is not known, and no other traces of life appear in the reefs. Except for the wind and the lapping of waves, the Beltian years were a quiet time, with none of the animal or vegetable life which flourished in the later geologic periods.

Lakes, ponds, and oceans are forever the depositories for the particles which were once rock. To make the story of Beltian time more real, we need only observe the sediments which have appeared during the span of a human life. These are arranged in the same layers and cleavage patterns as those anciently deposited.

The story of Belt time is absorbing not only because it is a fine example of sedimentary activity but because it represents a very early geologic period. However, there are many similar deposits in the Pacific Northwest whose history is even more interesting because of the fossils which they contain.

Nature's Fuel Bin

Man is a lover of warmth. Sometime during his evolution he learned that fire would warm his body. Much later he found that fire through fuel could generate power for machines and smelt the minerals he needed for his ingenious civilization. Coal proved to be a ready fuel.

Compared with the great fields of the East, the Pacific Northwest has little coal. Yet the same processes and climate which prevailed when the eastern veins were formed produced the coal deposits of the West. In numerous road-cuts in the Cascade Mountains, black veins of badly crushed material can be readily noticed. These are, in many cases, poor grade coal.

Man's geologic knowledge of coal evolved gradually. Finding plant stems, leaves, and even tree trunks imbedded in seams of coal, showed that coal was formed from vegetation. Further probing and digging revealed that coal deposits are basin-shaped, that is, the layers are thinnest at the edges and thickest at the center or deepest part. From these facts it was learned that dense vegetation growing in shallow, swampy areas is the source of today's coal deposits. One other clue gave proof of this. Under some coal beds, old roots were imbedded in the clay. This suggests that plants once grew in the coal basins, and—since more were found buried within the coal—it was logical that, as time went on, both living and dead vegetation accumulated in the basins. There had to be water in the swamps where the coal-forming vegetation grew because aquatic animal remains appeared with the plant life in coal seams.

Hydrogen, carbon, and oxygen are the chief components of plants. When a plant dies and decays, new substances result from the rotting tissues. For example, when a log decays in air, the hydrogen, carbon, and oxygen (plus oxygen from the air) unite to form carbon dioxide and water. Since both of these substances are easily carried away by the air, the plant in time disappears. When plants decay under water, as in swamps, a different reaction occurs. Under water there is little oxygen to form carbon dioxide and water. Instead, a carbon-hydrogen gas, called marsh gas, is formed. This marsh gas causes the rather offensive odor around the shorelines of lakes and ponds that contain much decaying vegetation. This process removes much of the hydrogen and oxygen but the carbon is only mildly affected. When this carbon mass hardens through compression, the product is coal.

Two conditions must exist for coal formation: large amounts of vegetation and decay under water. In the Paleozoic Era, inland seas—perhaps better classified as inland swamps—were choked with a profusion of plants, some of which were pulpy and rapid growing. There had to be a long period of mild climate to accumulate such an immensity of vegetation and to allow it to decay under water. Four hundred years is required to form a layer of coal one foot thick and some beds are fifty to sixty feet thick.

In the Pacific Northwest, coal is mined at Bellingham, Washington; and in the area east of Seattle, between Puget Sound and the Cascade Mountains—proof that these regions were once occupied by swamps containing dense coal-forming vegetation. Roslyn and Cle Elum, on the east slope of the Cascades, are coal-mining centers. Before the rise of the Cascade Mountains, these areas were low and swampy, no mountains robbing them of the warm, wet winds from the Pacific. The profuse vegetation was stored away in these basins to be transformed into coal.

A coal field approximately 250 miles in extent lies in the coastal region of Coos Bay, Oregon, where it is estimated that 200 million tons of coal can still be mined. Evidently for a long time, coal-forming plants and swamps existed in Oregon.

Ginkgo Petrified Forest

When Indians of Washington State's Columbia Plateau picked up pieces of petrified wood to fashion arrowheads, they likely never dreamed that this would some day be considered a unique fossil forest. Early explorers and trappers may have seen the deposits but they apparently gave them only passing notice. It remained for Professor George F. Beck of Central Washington State College, to discover this spectacular field in 1931. Of it he says, "No fossil forest in the world approaches the Ginkgo Forest in the kind of trees present. No other forest in the world is known to have been buried in liquid lava."

The buried forest became even more remarkable with the discovery, in hardest basalt, of ginkgoes, perhaps the world's oldest tree. Long ago the ginkgo was grown, and held sacred, in the temple gardens of Japan and China. But, beyond that, its fossil remains reach back 250 million years to the dawn of the age of reptiles. Yet it is still with us, thriving in many Northwest localities.

Discovery of the petrified trees in the Columbia basalt led to the incorporation of this area into the Ginkgo State Park located on U. S. Highway 10, a short distance west of the Columbia River at Vantage. Following one of the easy trails leading to the petrified logs is like a trip to the beginning of time.

The ginkgo trees flourished ten million years ago in a world not unlike the physical world of today. There were swamps in the Vantage vicinity where grew such water-loving trees as the cypress, now common in southern bayous. On drier land, grew gum trees, persimmon, and ash. Douglas Fir, so familiar in the rain forests of the Pacific Northwest today, thrived at higher elevations north of the Vantage area. These are only a few of the hundreds of trees which have been identified in fossil form. Eastern American hardwoods, Asiatic types such as the fan-leafed ginkgo, and a few subtropic species are all represented in the prehistoric woodlands of eastern Washington.

When, one after another, the petrified forms of the many species were discovered in the enveloping basalt, their secrets became the history of the Ginkgo Forest. Digging in the crumbling, stubborn basalt revealed that some trees like the cypress had rooted themselves in the prehistoric swamps. As their life cycle ended, they were buried in the in-gredients of the swamp. With continued digging, logs without roots or branches came to light among the rooted trees. The excavators determined to find out why.

To study the composition and structure of rocks scientifically, specimens must be brought to the laboratory. Here, microscope slides can reveal the elements that make up a particular specimen. By examining the cell structure and grain of petrified wood, the trained observer can name the kind of tree from which the samples came. Because of the odd fact that many of the petrified logs were rootless, these specimens were choice objects for study. Mag-nification revealed that they were once oak, larger than any existing today, and that they had not grown in the Vantage swamps.

Where did the oak come from? The direction had to be from the north because drainage through the area is from that direction. Being wood, the logs obviously must have been transported by water. Somewhere in the north country then, once stood a forest of great oaks. Exactly where it stood cannot be pinpointed but a map of present-day Washington gives a clue. It shows that the Okanogan is the only major valley with a north-south direction and a southern opening that would permit great volumes of water and floating objects to be projected almost directly toward Vantage.

Somewhere along this route grew the oaks now at Ginkgo State Park. Those who have studied the problem say this site was in the northern Okanogan Valley, quite possibly in that part extending northward into British Columbia. That primeval forest must have been an impressive sight with its tall straight trees supporting great canopies of leaves. Among the oaks there were likely some lesser hardwood species, lending their beauty to the prehistoric scene.

Today's apple trees and other deciduous trees and evergreens have replaced these ancient plants. Some fitful change of climate no doubt destroyed that northern oak forest. Using present-day tricks of the weather as a guide, we can put together a sequence of events that might have accomplished this destruction. First, in the Okanogan Valley and tributary areas, there might have been a heavy snow followed by a wind strong enough to twist and snap off oak trees. Since oaks are deep rooted, a great wind would likely tear down trees before the roots could be pulled loose. And, judging from the huge girth of the oak logs at Vantage, these trees must have reached maturity. If so, heart rot may have weakened them, making them less resistant to the savage wind.

How the trees were finally transported to the Okanogan Valley can be readily imagined. After the heavy snow, there might have been a spring flood— caused by warm spring weather and rains in the high altitudes of tributary watersheds. A fast thaw could have sent deep water rushing through the forest areas in the lowlands along the Okanogan River. Soon, with the trees afloat, the abnormal torrent could have tossed them against each other and against the rough bottom of the river bed. Branches and bark would disappear as they rolled and ground together. Churned about in the flood, the trunks could have become logs, peeled and smooth as they are now. (Such peeling took place just recently when a dam in a tributary of the Okanogan broke.)

When the ancient flood receded, timber would have been piled high on the flat where the water had left it. This is probably how the logs came to rest far from their native environment. Afloat for a time in the swampy ponds, they would finally have sunk, waterlogged, into the mud.

Mud and water were not the final coating on the logs which collected in the marshes of the region. These logs were destined to become encased in stone. With the advent of the Miocene Age—a period of extensive volcanism in the Pacific Northwest—the earth in the Vantage area was invaded by fluid lava which welled up out of the ground. The marshy places containing the logs and trees we see today as stone were gradually enveloped by the flowing lava.

The logs were no doubt partly or wholly petrified when the lava arrived. Some think that the molten rock hastened the process, as the heat would have changed the water to steam. The steam and vapor from the lava — charged with minerals and under great pressure from the weight of the liquid rock— penetrated the pores of the wood not already petrified, depositing the mineral particles which changed the woody cells into shiny stone. Five hundred feet of lava lay above the ginkgo forest at the end of the Miocene Age.

Alternating heat and cold and intermittent runoff of water slowly removed the upper layers of the lava that covered the petrified logs at Vantage. Gradually fragments, then portions, of the main sections of the logs were exposed. It is these logs that delight Pacific Northwest tourists.

Lava Cast Forest

Far to the south, in central Oregon, a lava flow demonstrates that in ancient times large trees grew in this part of the state. These trees are not petrified; they are not even present. Nevertheless, proof that they once existed shows clearly in the Lava Cast Forest, on U. S. Highway 97, south of Bend, Oregon (Photo No. 24).

In volcanic times, lava from the north side of Newberry Crater poured down into the surrounding countryside. When the moving lava advanced on the living forests it toppled and covered countless trees. Log casts occurred when the lava was held in place around the log long enough to harden and cool before the wood was consumed by the heat. Since the invasion of the lava, sufficient soil has built up to support another forest, at least in the Lava Cast area.

Leaves From An Ancient Garden

On slabs of sedimentary rock, fossil records of leaves, ferns, and other plants are often found pressed into prints that have outlasted the centuries. A record of prehistoric plants is occasionally revealed when fossil-bearing rock is broken.

Leaves of deciduous trees and many other leafy plants live for a summer, then fall to the ground. Here for a time the fallen foliage becomes a rustling carpet, but soon it decays, turning into powdery humus to enrich the earth around the plants that gave it life.

Photo No. 24   *Oregon State Highway Commission*

Lava cast of a prehistoric log in Lava Cast Forest on U. S. Highway 97, south of Bend, Oregon. Lava flowed through some Oregon forests in prehistoric time, enveloped and burned the logs, then left casts as a record of the event.

Trees standing on the edges of ponds drop their leaves in the water below. When the leaves of trees or plants fall into streams, the water transports them into ponds or lakes. Here, as on land, a great many of them decay and become part of the soft mud at the bottom of the pond or lake.

Under the right conditions, leaves sometimes become fossils. This process is an interesting one. First the leaves must settle unbroken to the bottom of a quiet body of water. Here a layer of mud must be gently laid over the vegetation, sealing it from rapid decay. Mud brought in by streams produces weight to make the soil at the bottom of the pond more compact. Should the process stop at this point, the leaves in the compact mud would probably never become the daintily-printed fossils sought by collectors. Additional pressure must be placed on the leaves either by the weight of the sediments brought in by the streams, or by upheaval of the earth, which compresses sedimentary formations. Under these conditions mud turns into shale.

Unearthed fossil leaves and other plant particles take on formations which represent ancient bottoms of lakes and ponds. The water that transported the specimens has vanished and the rock concealing the fossils may appear in a place having no relation to present bodies of water. The autumn day on which the leaves fell to the surface of quiet water is recorded in the leaves themselves, proving that such life was present long ago.

Slabs containing the graceful forms of bygone life are now frequently used for home decoration. These leaves from ancient gardens are often placed side by side with today's most colorful plants.

Fossil leaf collectors can discover good specimens of these plant remains at several accessible places in the State of Washington. They are most often found in close-layered black shale or sandstone. The outcrops of these along Chuckanut Drive, south of Bellingham, in Whatcom County, are rich in leaf fossils. Large palm leaf fossils have been found on the Nooksack River, on State Highway 1, a mile south of the Boulder Creek bridge. More leaves lie buried in the shale and sandstone, exposed in a roadcut east of Kelso, in Cowlitz County—less than a mile from the end of Allen Street Road. East of the

Cascade Mountains, fossil leaves appear at the roadside park on the old highway between Cashmere and Wenatchee. These are all in shale and sandstone beds. Farther east, half a mile above the mouth of Deep Creek, northeast of Spokane, sandy shales, once the bottom of a body of water, now hold these records of vegetation, trapped in their ancient mud.

John Day Fossil Beds

The State of Oregon is rich in fossil treasure. East of the Cascade Mountains in central Oregon, in what has been named the John Day Fossil Beds State Park, there are animal fossils in such great variety that the deposit has gained world renown. Many eastern museums display specimens from these John Day beds, so largely spread as to be included in several state park units. Five of these are along State Highway 19, which follows the John Day River between Kimberly and Picture Gorge. Two are on U. S. Highway 26, between Picture Gorge and the town of John Day. Another is in the Painted Hills area, ten miles northwest of Mitchell.

No one person deserves credit for the discovery of the John Day fossils. However, Thomas Condon, the early Northwest geologist, working at The Dalles in 1863, brought attention to them through a collection of fossils which he made — assisted by friends who knew of his interest.

This writer once had a notion that he should become a taxidermist. Soon his back porch became the depository for everything dead. Friends passing by from their hunting or hiking dropped what they had killed or found. In the interest of sanitation and domestic peace the project had to be abandoned. Condon had a similar but happier experience. Soldiers stationed at The Dalles, returning from missions into central Oregon, brought him countless fossils. On one occasion he secured permission to accompany them into the fossil areas. Soon his collection gained the attention of scientific men at eastern universities. It was only a matter of time until the area had been explored by scientific teams from many states of the nation, and by foreign fossil hunters as well.

The natural setting of the John Day basin has undergone many changes in the eons of time through which it has passed. Were it not that a variety of environments has existed in this part of Oregon, the kinds of fossils would be limited; favorable habitats have been provided, however, for dozens of widely different plants and animals. Likely for this reason the area is now popular with both paleontologists and "leisure-time" scientists.

An active visitor on the American continent in geologic time, the ocean once reached to the Blue Mountains, approximately 220 miles from the present seacoast. This area was then home for many fishes and animals of the sea. Sea shells from these ancient waters were among the first objects collected by Thomas Condon. Marsh-loving plants and animals also flourished during this time. As the waters receded, vegetation was abundant on the edges of lakes for herbivorous animals.

There were times when conditions in the John Day basin were quite arid. At one point in prehistoric time, volcanic eruptions did much to end the large amount of animal life. The area still has thick beds of volcanic ash; and, since many of the animal bones are encased in this volcanic material, it is reasonable to assume that it was the hot, suffocating ashes which destroyed the animals. Lava flows, the remnants of which still cap some of the fossil hills, blanketed many ash deposits.

Most recent of the geologic events in this region has been some uplift of the land and the down-cutting of the John Day River. Lakes which once extended across the land have since been drained. The persistent John Day River has cut canyons and gorges through the lava, the ashes, and some of the ancient lake beds. This river can actually be called the true discoverer of the fossils for, had the erosion not occurred, many of its ancient records would have remained hidden.

There are a number of especially good places in this area for hunting fossil souvenirs. On State Highway 19, opposite Milepost 119, is Turtle Cove—so called by Thomas Condon because land turtle fossils were found here. Early fossil hunters considered this the best fossil ground in the region. Turtles, however, were only minor members of the menagerie of animals whose bones were turned up in the rich fossil grounds of the cove. The cat family was represented by ten members, three of which were relatives of the saber-toothed tiger. Wolves, coyotes, and dogs were included. Most interesting, perhaps, were some of the first members of the horse family. Small as a dog, this early horse had three toes. Not until millions of years later did the horse grow in size and develop the solid hoof it has today. The rhinoceros and the camel were both found in the Turtle Cove area—strange partners even in fossil form. Oreodons were queer creatures compared with the animals of today but in the John Day area they are one of the most numerous species. Built much like a pig, and about its size, Oreodons were vegetarians and cud-chewers. No relatives of the Oreodon are alive today.

In the William Mascal Park unit—reached a mile south from Milepost 126.7—are the later John Day beds—later by twenty million years. These beds are covered with Columbia lava, which in turn is covered with the Mascal formation. Here more animal records appear but of a higher, better-developed fauna. Included are a more modern horse and the interesting mastodon of the Pleistocene elephant family.

Anyone wishing to see plant and fish fossils should visit the section about seven miles east of Dayville near Milepost 136. It is between the highway and the river and was once known as the Van Horn Ranch. Fossil perch can be found here as well as twenty-three distinct kinds of trees and plants.

Travelers who prefer land forms to fossils—if for no other reason than as photographic subjects—should watch for at least four places when traveling south from Arlington on State Highway 19. First of these is Davis Dike. A dike is a form taken by molten lava which has been injected into a fissure and, because softer materials have been eroded from both sides of it, its harder rock now stands as a wall. The Davis Dike crosses the John Day River and highway at Milepost 107, in a southeast-northwest direction. It can be traced for fifteen miles. Part of this dike is said to have columnar structure, but these columns now lie like piled wood. Some geologists believe that the Davis Dike represents one of the outlets from which was poured the lava that covers so much of central Oregon.

The Cathedral at Milepost 116 is one of the best viewpoints for the John Day formations. The Cathedral wears a cap of black basalt bedded in columns, typical of the Columbia flow occurring in so many places east of the Cascades. Beneath this

Photo No. 25 *Oregon State Highway Commission*

Here are John Day River and Highway, showing the Cathedral in the background with its jaunty black basaltic cap—one of the most famous rock formations in the John Day Fossil Bed country, where prehistoric animals once roamed in a tropical paradise.

rather jaunty basaltic cap, extending downward to the river, lie the John Day beds. These have been cut by hundreds of tiny rills of water and they wear a variety of pastel shades of blue and green. This is a good spot to use a color camera (Photo No. 25).

At Turtle Cove, Milepost 119, both the fossil hunting and scenery are excellent. In what has been named the Blue Basin of Turtle Cove is a tangled network of canyons, ravines, and gulches, the work of running water during heavy rains. Here the blue

Photo No. 26   *Oregon State Highway Commission*

Sandstone pillars to be seen between Fossil and Clarno, Oregon. Note the bedding of
sediments and the isolated position of these pinnacle clusters.

color is of a most delicate shade. Here pinnacled
peaks rise in complete symmetry. And here is silence
because all the animals which once roamed this land
have long since died. Their bones are now records
in a labyrinth of tinted hills.

Between Fossil and Clarno, Oregon, a thick layer
of severely-weathered sandstone has resulted in a
superb scenic and geologic attraction (Photo No.
26). So deep has the bedded rock been dissected

[116]

that the remnants of this once-extensive deposit now show grotesque shapes. Pillars, turrets, and cones, separated by deep and narrow chasms, are everywhere. Curiously enough, these formations are not solidly arranged. Rather, they stand as clusters of spires, between which are large vistas of sage-covered hills and slopes.

Immediately discernible is the bedded nature of the sandstone, deposited here when the ocean and later lakes covered eastern Oregon. These sandstone monuments are the record keepers of those times because in them lie the ancient fossils — striking proof that this area once teemed with strange animal creatures and exotic plants.

Washington Fossil Areas

"Gold is where you find it" and the same can be said of fossils. In places like the John Day basin, large numbers of plant and animal remains are concentrated, probably because of the ideal habitat nature provided there. However, fossils are apt to be found anywhere, especially where there is sedimentary rock representing the geologic periods which held life.

Since much of western Washington and Oregon has at times been inundated by the sea, large parts of this area have sedimentary rock, with considerable intrusion of igneous rock. Some sedimentary material was pushed upward among the complex materials forming the Cascades, so fossils can be found in them at high elevations. At Hart's Pass, in the northern Cascades, there are shell fossils found 6197 feet above sea level.

During its visits to various parts of the Northwest, the ocean left many kinds of fossil shells—all proof of its landward travel. A mountain in northern Skagit County, Washington, called Washington Monument, has revealed some interesting facts about the age when part of Washington rested below the sea. There are no trails in to this landmark but those who seek it out will find in it a key to three important geologic events in the history of the area.

The lowest exposed rock on Washington Monument is limestone, which reveals that this layer was formed under ocean water swarming with ocean life. Above the limestone is a layer of sandstone; this tells about a change in natural conditions of the age. The sand particles, of which sandstone is composed, were brought here by running water. This suggests that, during the deposition of the limestone, rivers and streams which were probably absent or very few in number, later increased in number and in the amount of erosion. The most interesting layer of sediments here is a layer of conglomerate resting on the sandstone of Washington Monument. This cemented material consists of large cobbles, some volcanics and some small pebbles—suggestive of dramatic and mysterious happenings. The land might have been lowered by sinking; certainly streams strong enough to carry or roll large fragments of rock poured into this shoreward area. Low-gradient streams do not carry large rock fragments; only swift-flowing streams draining mountain heights can perform such work. But what of the mountains whence these fragments came? Of these 250,000,000-year-old mountains we have no knowledge — we have only their pieces.

Because some of the animals living in this water needed sunlight, we know that the water in this area was comparatively shallow — only one hundred to three hundred feet. The shells of other warmth-loving creatures tell us that the water was warm enough for them to thrive. The area abounds in brachiopods, a kind of shellfish; bryozoans, moss-like animals common in some rocks in Europe; and a few poorly preserved corals, one of which strangely enough is found only in Asia. In some places the limestone is a solid mass of crinoids. These are sea lilies. They look like tulips but are really sea animals. Though in other parts of the world the "stems" of these animals reach a length of ninety feet, in the Skagit area they are only two feet long.

Although the John Day country in Oregon has the best fossil grounds in the Pacific Northwest, animals living in many of the seas of past geologic ages were left in the hardened mud when the Washington seas, or arms of them, receded.

Fossils from Cambrian time are found in Stevens and northern Pend Oreille counties. The origin of these is traceable to an arm of the sea which originated in California and stretched northward through Nevada, Utah, Idaho, eastern Washington and on through British Columbia to the Arctic. Trilobites are the most important fossils of the Cambrian period. They look like the modern sow bug. Brachiopods, which resemble clams, also lived in the Cambrian. The collector who wishes to distinguish between clams and brachiopods should remember that the two valves of a clam are identical, whereas the two valves of a brachiopod are different. The best places to look for trilobites and brachiopods in Washington are (1) in the Lehigh Portland Cement quarry, southeast of Metaline Falls, (2) near Addy in Stevens County, a short distance south from the west end of the Colville River bridge, and (3) about a half mile up the east fork of Stranger Creek from the bridge on the Dunn Mountain Road.

The Ordovician period was almost a repetition of the Cambrian since practically the same areas were flooded by the sea. Marine life was again plentiful but different kinds had evolved. This period featured graptolites, peculiar creatures whose fossils remind the finder of plant stems and leaves. Close examination of graptolite fossils reveals that they had no vascular system, whereas veins in leaves are well defined.

The best places to look for graptolites are (1) below the Pend Oreille Mine on the west side of the Pend Oreille River, about a mile north of Metaline Falls, (2) along the sides of Slate Creek, where it empties into the Pend Oreille River, about five miles northeast of Metaline Falls, and (3) where highway cuts occur about one mile south of Ledbetter Lake, in Pend Oreille County.

Animal fossils of the Devonian period are both east and west of the Cascade Mountains. During this period the San Juan Islands were under water and just about the same areas were inundated during the Cambrian and Ordovician periods. Brachiopods and corals were again prominent, much like those in the ocean today. One of them, the horn coral, is now extinct. Anyone wishing to see Devonian fossils should visit the hillside northwest of the road-crossing on Fence Creek in Pend Oreille County.

Brachiopods, corals and bryozoans continued into the Carboniferous period, which is subdivided into the Mississippian and Pennsylvanian. These were coal-forming periods. Bryozoans lived in colonies called zoariums, which occur either as incrustations on rock, in twig-like formations bearing countless pinhole openings; or as fans or fronds, perforated by the tiny holes in which these small animals lived. Bryozoans can be collected from the limestone in the low hills between Valley and Springdale; also a mile north of the Jumpoff School, along the Jackel Road, and a short distance south of the Stevens Road.

There may be a relation between the San Juan Islands and the northern Cascades because Permian fossils appear in both places, as well as near Kettle Falls in Stevens County. Directly north of Kettle Falls, snails and corals are imbedded in a hillside outcrop.

In the cold Triassic period, which began about 200 million years ago, sediments were laid in the San Juan Islands, and in the area now occupied by the Siskiyou, Klamath and Blue Mountains of Oregon. Both eastern and western Washington have Triassic formations. On Davidson Head on the northwest side of San Juan Island in Washington, fossil clams of the Triassic Age can also be found. Ferry County, east of the mountains, has two such deposits, one on the east side of Kettle River, three and a half miles south of Curlew on State Highway 4A; the other on the east side of the road leading into the upper Shasket Creek, one and a half miles from State Highway 4A.

The period called Cretaceous—meaning chalky —left many rocks in the San Juan Islands, that hold cephalopods and clam fossils in great numbers. A cephalopod is a tentacled mollusk, such as the octopus and squid. Sucia Islands, in the San Juans, produce two kinds of cephalopods; one is coiled, the other is straight.

The Tertiary period, which began sixty million years ago, lasted nearly all the Cenozoic Era. In this time great volcanic displays covered large areas of Washington and Oregon with igneous rock. Some Tertiary sea deposits are to be found on the west side of the Cascades. A number of sediments which were doubtless deposited in embayments of the sea appear at Black Diamond, Cle Elum, Bellingham, Morton, Packwood, and Wenatchee. Near Spokane, Tertiary Lake deposits are interbedded with Columbia basalt flows. These interbedded features are also scattered about the Columbia Basin and the Yakima Valley. Marine fossils of this age are the most abundant of any found in Washington. Among them are clams and oysters (pelecypods), tooth shells (scaphopods), and snails and limpets (gastropods). These lie scattered about the state. In the road banks along State Highway 9, between Porter and Malone, pelecypods are numerous, while the bluffs along the Strait of Juan de Fuca, especially west of West Twin River, offer good hunting for pelecypods and gastropods.

Excavations west of the Cascades have unearthed many specimens of recent origin which can hardly be called fossils, yet are records of plants and animals as much as those encased in rock. Excavators in Seattle once found a log of large diameter covered by about sixty feet of glacial sand and gravel. This was evidence that, considering the long periods of time, glaciers in this region had only recently retreated. At another site, which was being prepared for the foundation of an office building, a bone of a prehistoric animal was uncovered at considerable depth. A scientist who visited the place remarked that the bone was eleven million years old. A workman spoke up, "I personally don't believe it has been here over ten million years."

Fossils of vertebrate animals are fairly rare in Washington. Most of those discovered have been east of the Cascades, where arid conditions slow down weathering of these fossils that have been uncovered by erosion. Some vertebrate bones have been uncovered along the east side of the Columbia River, near Ringold, north of Richland; others in the sand and silt on both sides of the Wenas Valley, Yakima County. The bones found in Washington are usually those of cold weather animals such as the mammoth, caribou, and bison. Near Port Angeles, the bones of a small mastodon were discovered by a farmer digging for a reservoir.

The writer once helped unearth the remains of a primitive elephant from a hillside near Cheney, Washington. The story of how the skeleton of this prehistoric elephant was found illustrates the events which often lead to the discovery of these interesting specimens.

The elephant had died in an area where soil now covers the Columbia basalt. His body had been covered shortly afterwards by river-washed soil, by wind-borne particles, or by volcanic ash. As the centuries passed, the hillside which contained the grave was eroded bit by bit, bringing the surface of the ground closer and closer to the bones. Then one day a farmer who was plowing this field found that his plow had encountered and partly dislodged a large bone. His curiosity led to the digging. His admonition was, "You can dig if you refill the hole." The skeleton had remained near the ground surface too long for the bones to be intact. They crumbled in the air. The teeth and tusks, made of harder stuff, were removed—and the hole was filled.

One of the basalt flows in the Grand Coulee of Washington yielded an important piece of evidence regarding the kind of life existing when the Columbia Plateau was made. Not content to cover logs, trees and minor plants, this flow killed a rhinoceros, then made a cast of the body for the record. The rhino is thought to have been covered by highly-fluid and rapid-moving basalt. Before he could find an avenue of escape, he was trapped and destroyed. The fluids within the animal cooled and hardened the lava so that the cast took the shape of the rhino's body. Today, near Blue Lake in the Grand Coulee, the positions of the legs are marked by four cylindrical holes in the basalt, and the rounded contour of the body is arched over the leg cavities. One side of the cavity is open, disclosing the shape of the animal.

This site is at the north end of Blue Lake and a boat must be used to reach the spot. Landing should be made at the talus slope at the bottom of a rocky point which projects into the lake. At the first ledge above this point the climber reaches a flat on which once grew a sizable forest. On that shelf are the hollow molds of tree stumps consumed by the hot lava when it flooded this part of eastern Washington. The once-fiery tomb of the rhinoceros is in the next higher ledge, and another tree cast is located beyond the rhino cave at a somewhat higher elevation.

Ghost Forest in Clear Lake

Lava flows have left numerous records of their activities in the Pacific Northwest, and when they did it was on a grand scale. Flowing lava leaves no doubt about its origin or about what it did during its existence.

There is a record of a lava flow — perhaps as recently as a thousand years ago—which streamed from the Belknap Crater in central Oregon, to perform an engineering feat in record time. This lava flow traveled westward into the valley of the upper McKenzie River, where it made a dam of rough and jumbled stone. But, when the rock had cooled, the dam had permanence and it was watertight.

Water of sparkling clearness built up behind the dam, creating Clear Lake, 910 feet at its greatest depth, with an elevation of 3030 feet, and covering an area of two square miles. The lake can be reached by traveling north from Belknap Springs Junction. En route to Clear Lake from this point one passes three waterfalls pouring over basalt cliffs, one of which is fifty feet high.

The flowing lava from Belknap both created and destroyed. It created Clear Lake and drowned the forest of fir and cedar trees growing in the impounded area. These are now members of the ghost forest which stands beneath the quiet water of Clear Lake. Gliding over the water, one can look down at ghostly trees, two or three feet in diameter, devoid of leaves and bark, with branches reaching up in scarecrow fashion. These are the same species which still thrive on the hillsides above the lake level—but these were destined to become ghost trees through one of the upheavals of nature for which Oregon is famous.

Klickitat Lake

A similar occurrence created Klickitat Lake near Waldport, on the Oregon Coast, but no lava took part in its creation. This lake was made by a landslide which obstructed the drainage in an upland depression. Water from streams that collected in the hollow formed Klickitat Lake, partly submerging trees that grew in the flooded area. Sections of their trunks still stand as stumps in the lake (Photo No. 27).

Nature Keeps the Record of Man

Early Indians left their picture writing on the flat faces of a number of cliffs in the Pacific Northwest, as well as on several islands in the Columbia

Klickitat Lake near Waldport, on the Oregon Coast, was made by a landslide which obstructed the drainage in an upland depression. Water from streams that collected in the hollow to form the lake also partly submerged the trees growing in the area. Sections of their trunks still stand as stumps in the lake.

River. For what reason these picturesque symbols were made, or what purpose they served, has never been definitely established. Their meanings cannot be deciphered with certainty. If they contain intelligible messages, then these were understood only by the race of men who made them. They must therefore represent a group of people living in the Pacific Northwest long before the Indians began transmitting their legends from generation to generation.

One legend about these pictographs relates that when boys reached early manhood, some feat of

Photo No. 28   *Oregon State Highway Commission*

One of the best places in the Pacific Northwest to examine Indian pictographs is Picture Gorge, a short distance from Dayville, on U. S. Highway 26, in Oregon's John Day country. The pictures appear to be of men. Below them are circles, arcs, and strange figures.

courage, or endurance, had to be performed to qualify them for tribal membership. It was customary for a young man, upon reaching the proper age, to strike out alone on a long journey, beset by privation and danger. At the farthest point from his home he selected a flat-surfaced rock, usually the face of a cliff, and there recorded his journey, his encounters with wild animals, and the dangers he had met and conquered. This was acceptable evidence that he had traveled a long and hazardous route alone and that the events which he portrayed were true.

Doubters could visit the far place and see the writings for themselves.

One of the best places to examine Indian pictographs is Picture Gorge, a short distance from Dayville, on U. S. Highway 26, in Oregon's John Day country (Photo No. 28). The pictures appear to be of men. Below them are circles, arcs, and strange figures.

The shell mounds along the Oregon Coast also hold interesting records of ancient people. Long before Oregon was known to white men, Indians presumably came to this coast for food supplied by the sea. It was their custom to remove the edible portions of shell fish at central locations, possibly for protection. The discarded shells accumulated in great piles along the beach. Though weathered by time, great heaps of these shell mounds remain today (Photo No. 29).

A collection of such shells was uncovered by workmen building a public park at Bremerton, Washington. Among the shells was a human skeleton, perhaps one of those responsible for the accumulation of shells at this place.

New Eras Ahead

It is only through the study of a variety of nature's records that the story of ancient times can be recorded, or even recent times for that matter. The Pacific Northwest abounds in preserved specimens which tell the events of other days. Petrified wood is plentiful along the Columbia and, throughout the region, shell and plant fossils are encased in many of the sedimentary deposits. There is real pleasure in determining the kind of wood represented by a petrified specimen; also in trying to picture the environment where the species grew.

Photo No. 29   *Oregon State Highway Commission*

One of several shell mounds found along the Oregon coast—where Indians came for seafood. They would remove the edible portions at central locations, possibly for protection.

Shell fossils abound in the John Day and Puget Sound regions, in scattered sections of the Cascade Mountains, and in many places along the Pacific Coast. Finding such a fossil-rich area means that here is a place where ancient forms of life played their part in the geologic drama. Knowing that the Pacific Northwest was at least partly inundated several times in past ages, one could expect to find records of bygone life in low-lying areas. Finding these, then, at high elevations in the Cascade Mountains, is especially interesting, for this is proof of enormous uplift and also of the presence of the sea far from today's coastline.

We have not witnessed enough of the Quaternary period to comprehend what the ever-changing earth holds in store. In fact, we have just emerged from a series of glacial periods, the marks of which are still fresh on our landscape. The incredible slowness of inundations and uplifts does not permit man, during his brief sojourn on earth, to see any major geologic changes in their entirety.

Are new eras ahead? According to the records of past eras and the small-scale indications of continuing change which we see around us, the answer is decidedly yes. Already the North Sea, the Baltic Sea, and Hudson Bay have begun flooding. This could be the modest introduction of a new cycle of inundations and the subsequent disappearance of large sections of uplifted continents. It is still too early to know.

Chapter 7

OUR VOLCANIC LAND

Could our geologic history be enacted on stage, spectators would be struck by the continuity in the unfolding of geologic time. They would see land forms being uplifted, then eroded; ocean water creeping silently over barren peneplains, and prehistoric marine life stirring in the muddy ocean bottom. Climates would change; howling, icy storms would grip the landscape in cold and snow; then would come warmth enough to nurture verdant vegetation in tepid swamps. The periods of volcanic activity would be the most exciting of all. These might be called the angry moods of nature, for whole landscapes would be blotted out by lava pouring from earth vents—or blasted skyward by the terrifying roar of volcanoes. When such events had ceased, the rearranged landscape would have a fresh, new aspect.

No other part of the United States has volcanoes in the number found in the Pacific Northwest. In fact, some large areas elsewhere have none. These grand peaks, nature's most spectacular land forms, stand as monumental mountains in this region. There are places in the world, such as Africa, where all that remains of former volcanoes is some rocky plugs in the ground. The superstructures have been entirely worn down and carried away. In a number of these old volcanic conduits, though, nature stored one of the most precious of substances—diamonds.

The outstanding feature of Pacific Northwest volcanoes is their youthful appearance. Although erosion on them from ice and streams has been severe, they still have massive size and height. Eons must pass before these proud peaks will be reduced to puny hills.

Mount Rainier

Because of its size and splendor among mountains, early Indians named this peak, "The Mountain That Was God." Sighting this snow-covered giant in 1792, Captain George Vancouver gave it its present name in memory of his friend, Rear Admiral Peter Rainier. This volcanic giant dominates the many mountains of western Washington (Photo No. 30).

Now the highest volcano in the United States, Rainier once blazed among a line-up of fiery beacons along the Cascade Mountain crest. Aligned with it are Mounts Baker, St. Helens, Hood, and famous old Mazama, which now holds Crater Lake. These have all built towering cones of volcanic material on the top of the Cascades, which were already arched and uplifted into one of the major mountain barriers in the world.

Great as the Cascades are, they are dwarfed to foothills in comparison with the great peak of Mount Rainier, which serves as a landmark for those living on Puget Sound, a hundred miles away. Visible at even greater distances from points in eastern Washington, its white crown rises 14,408 feet above sea level and its base covers an area of one hundred square miles. Only Mount Whitney (elevation 14,495

Photo No. 30

Mount Rainier in western Washington once blazed among a line-up of fiery beacons along the Cascade Mountain crest. Now the highest volcano in the United States, its glaciered walls rise 14,408 feet above sea level

feet) in California and Mount Elbert (elevation 14,-431) in Colorado, surpass Rainier.

The history of Mount Rainier is much like that of volcanoes the world over. First, the Cascades were formed by the arching of the land, aided by the intrusion of igneous granites disturbing the sedimentary rocks of a wide coastal plain. They were then eroded into sharp peaks and deep valleys, appearing much as they do today. Next came the explosive rumblings of fire-laden rock, cracking open the huge crest of the Cascade ridge. Smoke and dust suddenly and noisily belched forth in the silent region.

Through the centuries that followed, eruption of cinders, shredded particles of lava, steam and occasional flows of liquid lava, merged and became solid layers on Rainier's ever-rising cone. At first, liquid andesite lava—a gray, acid rock—appeared. Then, as activity subsided, volcanic ash, cinders and fragmental materials were blown out.

Some geologists think that Mount Rainier may have attained an elevation of sixteen thousand feet. That, of course, was before the explosion which removed about two thousand feet from the top. There is some geologic evidence to support this theory. There is also a story in Indian legends of a great eruption. Known eruptions occurred in 1843, 1854, 1858, and, the last, in 1870. Rainier is now dormant except for jets of steam in the crater which melt the ice and snow around them. When caught on the summit by storms or darkness, mountaineers have kept from freezing by remaining by or near these steaming areas.

From the air, the mountain seems to be clutched in the arms of some gigantic marine monster. These apparent tentacles are glaciers, twenty-six in all, which radiate outward and downward from the fields of snow. Forty square miles of the summit and sides of Mount Rainier are blanketed in glacial ice. Six glaciers have entrenched their ice in deep troughs extending far beyond the base of the volcano. In fact, it is believed that some of the glaciers of Mount Rainier once occupied parts of the Puget Sound area. Since the glaciers cannot extend themselves beyond today's snow fields, they are gradually receding. Only on high mountains where heavy snowfall occurs do glaciers still exist. The empty U-shaped troughs in the lower altitudes now carry glacial rivers muddied by the upper carving which is still at work.

Mount Rainier National Park contains a glacier, also an empty trough where it once worked. These can be reached by State Highway 5 at the Nisqually River entrance. En route to Paradise Valley, 5.4 miles from Longmire, the park highway crosses the headwaters of the Nisqually River, which emanates from the snout of Nisqually Glacier, only a few hundred feet upstream from the bridge. There Nisqually lies, dirtied by the rolling rock and soil of the valley walls. Downstream is a confusion of glacially-deposited rock, mute evidence of glacial activity in the Nisqually trough. Here one is right in the middle of a glacial valley, only yesterday emptied of its tremendous burden of ice.

Paradise marks the end of all travel by car. Possibly this is just as well, for there is much to see. Here, at 5557 feet above sea level, Mount Rainier towers almost 9000 feet over the general level of the Cascade crest. Lying in the gravel near Nisqually bridge, 10,500 feet lower than its source, Nisqually Glacier descends the scarred walls of the mighty mountain in shimmering blue ice—ice supplied endlessly by winter's inevitable blizzards. At intervals, deep crevasses show on the glacier, resulting from the passage of ice over rock masses that have not yielded to mountain scouring. Despite its present grandeur, Nisqually is failing and some day will likely disappear. Though it moves twenty-five feet a month, its lower extremity cannot continue its progress down the Nisqually Valley because of the warmer temperatures of this age. Each year finds the end of this glacier higher up in its trough.

Imposing as it is, the structure of Mount Rainier does not have the pattern of a perfect cone. It is broad and massive, with rocky roots spreading down the slopes of the Cascades. Its top is broken and irregular from outpourings of liquid lava that flowed down its sides. Fresher materials to the northeast indicate that area to have been the scene of Rainier's last eruption. The crater atop this snowy sentinel is two miles across. After the major eruptions had subsided, later and feebler eruptions formed two small cinder cones within the main crater. These were built up until they joined and actually became higher than the original rim. This feature is not evident when viewing Rainier from western Washington.

To the south, across Paradise Valley, lies the Tatoosh Range, as rugged a collection of peaks and ridges as exists anywhere. Deeply scarred by ancient glaciation, their knife-like ridges and pointed peaks offer good climbing, photography, and sightseeing.

Mount Rainier is easy to reach. "Just keep looking at it and drive toward it," says a man at a corner grocery, a hundred miles away. This is usually successful when driving along a highway with the mountain in sight. U. S. Highway 410 — one of the trans-Cascade highways connecting Tacoma on the coast and Yakima in eastern Washington—enters the northern corner of the Mount Rainier National Park and travels for some distance through it. On the west side, a network of good roads out of Seattle, Tacoma, Olympia and points south, all direct motorists to Rainier.

Residents of the Pacific Northwest are lucky because volcanic peaks, with their recreational areas, are near the centers of population. Bellingham has Mount Baker; Seattle, Tacoma, and Olympia have Mount Rainier; Longview has the wilderness area of Mount St. Helens; and Portland has Mount Hood. Those living in the cities and towns of southern Oregon may vacation at Mount Mazama in Crater Lake National Park.

Glacier Peak

So named because from its summit fifty glaciers can be counted within a radius of thirty miles, Glacier Peak is a lonely, extinct volcano, surrounded by a beautiful array of other Cascade peaks. With an elevation of 10,568 feet, it towers over exciting topography in a superb wilderness area, where no roads have as yet been built. Only Forest Service trails permit the foot-traveler to see this little-known giant just north of the 48th parallel, near the main Cascade divide. It is almost due east of Everett, Washington. Here in this crisp, alpine setting one can discover the workings of glaciers and the contour of naked, solidified lava, which once slid down the slopes of Glacier Peak.

One feat alone distinguishes Glacier Peak from its neighbors. It once produced a tremendous eruption of pumice which fell all over the northern Cascades — extending to faraway southern Alberta. Pumice deposits attributable to this eruption are commonplace in the Entiat and Chelan valleys and on all mountain slopes and valleys surrounding this once-mighty volcano.

Mount Baker

Mount Baker might be called the northwestern corner post of the United States, for no other volcano is so near this extremity; and, as a geographical marker, no better land form could be found. Its beautiful snow-clad summit caps an almost perfect cone, built of lavas and tuffs ejected from the crater which lies 10,750 feet above the sea. It is composite in character, that is, its sides have stratified layers of flows and fallen explosive rock.

Along the road leading to the recreational area on the lower ski slopes, can be seen lava flows arranged in columnar structure. Some of the flows, which are andesite, show sections of columns distorted by bending. This is one of the features resulting from the cooling of molten rock. The early geologic history of the picturesque peak is not clear but this detracts little from the enjoyment that it provides for throngs of people.

The Twin Sisters Peaks, which lie south of Mount Baker, have interesting color and a unique composition. The rock of these peaks is orange on the surface but green when broken. This sharp-featured land form was once a sizable mass of igneous olivine —which is green—pushed up near the surface and later uncovered by erosion. Iron oxide caused the orange stain. It is worth noticing that these peaks are devoid of vegetation whereas neighboring mountains are heavily timbered. The cause is found in the rock composition of the Twin Sisters. It contains chromium oxide, poisonous to plants.

Mount Adams

When Lewis and Clark saw Mount Adams in south central Washington, they decided it was "the highest pinnacle in America." This, of course, proved to be incorrect. They were looking at the second highest peak in the Pacific Northwest (elevation 12,307 feet), Mount Rainier being the highest. Mount Adams is a much older volcano than even Mount Hood; its history is unlike that of any of the other

Pacific Northwest volcanoes, and its location is farther to the east—on the summit of one of the eastern Cascade ranges.

Volcanoes usually build symmetrical cones, with graceful, sloping sides, down which course the ashes and fragmental material blown out of the central crater. Mount Adams lacks such symmetry. Its sides are fluted with prominent dikes, causing deep indentations and irregular slopes. Since some of its upper escarpments are too steep to support glaciers, ice must form at the bottom of these steep cliff faces. Instead of having the rounded form of the typical volcano, Adams is a long ridge with a complex collection of several cones, all seemingly leaning on one another. It is evident that Mount Adams was built of lava flowing from many craters, each perhaps active in successive ages.

Mount Adams has other volcanic features adding to its exotic nature and its rugged make-up. These are volcanic vents more recent than those which built the mountain proper. About a hundred blowholes and parasitic cones are scattered about the slopes of this ancient giant. Some of these miniature volcanoes have all but disappeared through the ceaseless work of erosion. Their softer outer shells have been torn away, leaving the harder cores standing like monuments. From other vents, lava—which became sheets of rock — spewed out over a large area. The rock is still fresh, so much so that even the seeds of hardy subalpine trees have not been able to sprout and grow here.

Much of the country about Mount Adams has been visited by comparatively recent lava flows. The land upon which the flows rest was an ancient and heavily forested landscape. Some of its ancient rock is exposed beneath the newly-laid covering, and the existence of ancient trees is attested by the thousands of tree casts found in the lava. Rivers of molten rock flowed into stream channels, filling and deepening them. Lava being a poor conductor of heat, the tops of the lava flows cooled more rapidly, forming a solid crust. Underneath, however, the molten mass still flowed. In many instances, if the grade on which it ran was sufficiently steep, it burst out at the lower extremity, leaving in its wake a rocky, solidified tube. In time, as the surface flows weathered, appeared openings into which man peered, then entered and explored.

Water, too, is an explorer. Many of the tubes have been entered by water, so many have been partly or wholly filled with sediments. Some of the more newly-opened caverns contain countless chambers, caves, and galleries in which grotesque volcanic forms are preserved. Ice caves are common in the Pacific Northwest and the Mount Adams field has many of these which might even be called "ice factories." In pioneer days, several river towns along the Columbia, as far as The Dalles and Portland, secured ice from the Trout Lake Caves.

Sun-tinted snow on a distant volcano is a worthy subject for the photographer of scenic geology—but climbing the slopes of one of these vast piles of erupted rock will supply a wealth of material for a treasured picture story. From the timberline on either side of Mount Adams, it takes about six or seven hours of vigorous climbing to reach the top. During the climb it will become noticeable that, among the many features exhibited from ever loftier heights, the chief ingredient of this peak is lava. No central crater will come into view as the summit is reached. The summit is a mile-long ridge, the storage ground for the snow which nourishes Adams,

Klickitat, Lyman, and White Salmon glaciers. Other glaciers, namely Avalanche, Lava, Mazama, Pinnacle and Rusk, begin at a lower elevation because the sheer cliffs above them arc too steep to hold their neve fields.

From the summit ridge of Mount Adams one can look down several thousand feet to cirque ice fields which supply the ice and the power for the movement of the glaciers. Perhaps will be heard the awesome roar of avalanche ice as it leaves the heights and falls from the cliffs to the glaciers below. Since the summit area above the glaciers is famous avalanche ground, the visitor is almost certain to see, or hear, the avalanches, especially in early summer when the accumulated snow of winter loosens and falls.

The comparison of glacier characteristics is interesting. On Mount Adams, glaciers occupy a setting peculiar to this mountain. Two of them, Rusk and Klickitat, are in deep canyons; the rest are wider, fanning out on the bottom slopes. The lower ice limit on Adams is a considerable distance above 6500 feet. This comparatively high level can be explained by its location in the more arid part of Washington.

One wonders why Rusk is so deeply entrenched in its flume-like trough while the other glaciers are wider and shallower. It is believed that this glacier may have worked its way down into one of the hollow lava tubes, common in the area. By grinding off the roof of a lava tube, Rusk may have entered a ready-made channel. Klickitat Glacier, two miles in length, has cut its own larger canyon. Geologists point to the cirque feeding this glacier as one of the most splendid natural amphitheaters in America. This one and the larger cirque which spawns Carbon

Glacier on Mount Rainier, are classic examples of mountain cirques. The Klickitat cirque is a mile wide; ice comes to it from two ice streams which originate at the summit.

A portion of the original surface of Mount Adams is found rising a thousand feet from the floor of Hellroaring Canyon and is known as the Ridge of Wonders. This canyon was occupied by the Mazama Glacier, its receded form still lying on the upper slopes of the trough. Here, from Ridge of Wonders, is afforded a spectacular view of the eastern side of the mountain with its steep precipices, its dikes and glaciers. Little Mount Adams, a well-formed parasitic cone, is a fine picture subject, as are the curious forms of volcanic bombs, scattered over the ridge.

The northwest side, which no doubt receives more moisture, supports the largest glacier on Mount Adams—Adams Glacier, three miles long. This side has precipitous ice falls and ice rivers which drop half a mile to the reservoir supplying Adams Glacier. It is a wild and altogether fantastic realm of ice and snow, ever trying to escape to lower levels on its return to the sea whence it came.

Mount St. Helens

This mountain is young, symmetrical, and considered by some to be the most beautiful volcano in the Pacific Northwest. Named by Captain George Vancouver after Lord St. Helens, a diplomat, it lies 9671 feet above sea level.

St. Helens was not erected on the summit of the Cascades as were Mounts Hood and Adams. Its location is west of any Cascade ranges—where valley bottoms are about a thousand feet above the sea. Since St. Helens is surrounded only by low hills, its entire height of almost ten thousand feet is strikingly displayed. The country skirting this mountain is one of lakes and rivers, with plenty of room for outdoor recreation.

Lava flows, much like those which constructed Mount Adams, built the newcomer, St. Helens. Whereas the flows of Adams were thrown out of several craters, St. Helens owes its symmetry to its centralized activity. Beginning in 1830 and continuing intermittently to 1857, it erupted smoke and light ashes. The sky itself above the volcano was darkened—and ashes fell at The Dalles. Once, during this period, beginning in December, 1843, eruption continued for eighty-three days.

There are extensive new flows on the south and west sides of the mountain and more between these and the North Fork of Lewis River. On the west, the flows reached Goat Mountain. When they surrounded the "Buttes," these became islands in a river of liquid rock. One flow dammed a stream channel to create Lake Merrill. Other flows engulfed a virgin forest. These flows are thought to represent one of the latest episodes in the volcanic flooding of the Columbia Basin.

The lava beds just mentioned are posed in a wild array of disorder and violence. Now solidified and still, these formations vividly portray the chaos associated with their origin. Some of the stony rivers reveal that swift-flowing currents of fiery liquid were a reality. Some are rope-like, twisted, or convulsed in eddies; others cataract down over ancient rocks in sticky, nondescript lumps. There are underground galleries and, where trees were destroyed, tree casts give the dimensions of the long-gone woody trunks. Local residents, likely thinking of another violent realm, named various features

"Hell's Kitchen," "Devil's Punch Bowl," "Satan's Stairway"—and the names are appropriate.

In comparison with the glaciers of Rainier and Hood, those of Mount St. Helens are insignificant, only several broad, short ones occupying quite shallow beds. Forsyth Glacier, the most prominent, flows from the crater on the northwest side.

Below the snowline on slopes that have not been hidden by lava flows, there are fields of pumice in which large, angular boulders are imbedded, scattered here and there in haphazard arrangement. These boulders provide the key to a part of the history of St. Helens which has been enacted by no other volcano in the Pacific Northwest. The boulders were torn out of the Tertiary foundation, upon which the volcano came into being, then were hurled into space. As the volcano enlarged its diameter, more of these blocks were loosened and blown out so suddenly that they landed on the outer slopes unmelted and unchanged.

Mount Hood

Had man with his airplane been in existence when the volcanoes of the Cascades were active, these would have served as beacons for north-south flights along the mountain range. Their smoke by day and red flares at night, at fairly regular intervals, would have helped him navigate the skies. Mount Hood would have been one of these beacons. Today it is part of the series of Cascade volcanoes used as landmarks by fliers on clear days (Photo No. 31). Like other volcanoes in Oregon and Washington, Hood was erected on the backbone of the Cascades. The original site was almost four thousand feet in elevation, but successive eruptions built a towering cone. Hood grew, though, by shooting

Photo No. 31   *Oregon State Highway Commission*

Mount Hood seen from Horseshoe Bend on the Mount Hood Loop Highway, Oregon.
Its cone, badly damaged by erosive "vandals," is a mere remnant of the original shape.
Far down to the right and left of the ridge can be seen giant portions of the broken
crater walls.

out scoria, or slag, rather than by ejecting flows of
lava such as those which were part of the history
of Mount Rainier. The base of Hood is about seven
miles in diameter from east to west, and the mountain is probably of Miocene Age. No one knows how
high volcanic material extended upward when eruptions ceased. Today its altitude is 11,245 feet. Like
Rainier, Hood has jets but, unlike Rainier, these are
found in Crater Rock, a formation on the side of the
mountain.

Mount Hood was discovered in the days when
European countries sent out expeditions to explore
and annex new lands for their respective sovereigns.
On October 29, 1792, Lieutenant William Robert

Broughton, a member of Vancouver's expedition, representing His Majesty George III, was at the mouth of the Willamette River on the Columbia. He saw Mount Hood's great white crown in the southeast and gave it the name it now bears, in honor of Rear Admiral Samuel Hood, an officer in the British Admiralty who had served with distinction in the American and French Revolutions. It was sixty-two years before anyone looked down from that peak on the surrounding country. On August 14, 1854, a party under the leadership of William Barlow made the first successful ascent.

There are eight glaciers on the mountain's symmetrical sides, reaching down to six thousand feet above sea level. Since Mount Hood was formed chiefly of volcanic ash, it shows the deep entrenchment of glaciers and stream channels. The soft ashes have been cut to bottom level and even the underlying, ancient rocks of the Cascades themselves have been attacked. Mount Hood glaciers are not record breakers in size; they are renowned for their variety of classic glacial features, such as ice falls, crevasses, terraces, seracs, castles and pinnacles.

The cone of Mount Hood has been so severely damaged by erosive "vandals" that it is now little more than a remnant of its original shape. It is torn and broken by ice formed when the heat of the crater could no longer defend itself from the heavy, annual snowfalls. All that remains of the peak's broken crater is a narrow ridge, about a quarter of a mile long. The rest of the circular rim, which was once about a half mile in diameter, has been wrenched away. Far down to the right and left of the ridge can be seen giant portions of the crater walls which have been named Illumination Rock and Steels Cliff. No other parts of the walls are visible.

In the center and far below is a towering cone of lava. Its rock is harder than the scoria and andesite of which most of the mountain is composed. This is the solidified core of the volcano, a residual plug left when the volcano died. The core is surrounded by the softer materials which, for five miles, slope down the south side from the remaining north rim, almost to Government Camp. On the slope, beginning just below the north rim, flow two of the mountain's glaciers. Zigzag is on the west and White River Glacier passes Crater Rock on the east.

Some climbers like to think that a gigantic explosion removed the south side of the volcano. This is not likely because the solid state of Crater Rock, the core, indicates that Mount Hood was not in eruption when it was removed. The rim, weaker in composition than the other Pacific Northwest volcanoes, was doubtless broken down by the great weight of the ice and rock which accumulated within and on the crater. The resulting ice and rock slide would have been another tremendous spectacle. What seem to be its remains are now a notable part of the scenic geology of the Northwest. Somehow forests were ground into splinters and buried, canyons were obliterated, and the southwest side of the mountain suddenly supported a fan-shaped slope of ice, ashes, rock, and broken trees. The observer who trains his binoculars on the foot of the debris, below the glaciers, will see that streams have begun their attack on the huge slide. Deep ravines are already cut, remindful that more damage is in store for this beautiful Oregon land form.

The glaciers of Mount Hood have certain unique characteristics. Looking down on the slopes where the glaciers radiate, one sees that they have not dug deep valleys such as those on Mount Rainier, in which glaciers can survive at an average elevation of four thousand feet. In contrast, those of Hood rest in shallow, unfilled troughs, between which lie as many as three ridges of lateral moraine that spell out successive advances and retreats of mountain glaciers. Some of these are now fifty to a hundred feet higher than the level of existing glaciers—conclusive evidence that present-day glaciers are drastically shrunken compared with periods when they flowed even with the brim of their moraines. Yet, these periods are not too far removed, judging from the barren gravel slopes reaching up from the receding ice. Alpine glaciation, ever eager to take root on newly-exposed surfaces, has not yet begun to grow in the scanty soil of these high, ice-carved valleys.

Surrounded by beautiful evergreen forests and splendid camping and skiing facilities, Hood has the distinction of being the only volcano in the Pacific Northwest with a highway built entirely around its lower elevations. U. S. highway 26 out of Portland and State Highway 35 from Hood River offer quick, easy access to the area. Oregon has many scenic drives, and this is among the best. Glacial and volcanic features are evident at every turn. For those who wish to see them at close range, they can be reached by hiking from any one of innumerable places along the highway.

Mount Mazama—Crater Lake

Crater Lake, cupped in the burned-out cone of old Mount Mazama, is one of the greatest scenic attractions of the West (Photo No. 32). The route to this southern Oregon volcano is made easy by sev-

Photo No. 32   *Oregon State Highway Commission*

Cupped in Mount Mazama's ancient cone, Crater Lake's dazzling blue waters curl about lovely Wizard Island. Oddly enough, it is not a crater lake at all because it occupies a caldera far larger than the original crater of this southern Oregon mountain.

eral roads leading off both north-south U. S. Highways, 97 and 99. So famous has Crater Lake become that the mountain Mazama holds only secondary interest. No glaciers now mark the slopes of Mazama, though all other Pacific Northwest volcanoes are being eroded by glacial ice.

Both Crater Lake and Mount Mazama have mammoth proportions. The mountain is 6177 feet in elevation, with a nearly circular crater six miles across and twenty-one miles around. A rim road exposes every angle of the steep crater walls which vary from one to two thousand feet in height. The solidified lava is two thousand feet below the startling blue water. All is very quiet now where once belched fiery gases, sharp-edged cinders, and molten rock.

The volcano of Mount Mazama followed the pattern of all others of its time. Sporadic eruptions slowly enlarged the vent and its rising cone. That these eruptions were intermittent is proved by the fact that charred logs and stumps of trees are interbedded in the layers of volcanic material on the sides of the volcano. Sufficient time had to elapse between some of the eruptions to allow tree seeds to be transported to the ash beds, then take root and grow to considerable size before being enveloped by another eruption of lava. Geologists say that Mazama was an energetic builder. Some believe that it once reached a height of fourteen thousand feet. If this is true, its cone long ago was among the highest in the Northwest.

Excavators, working on the sides of Mazama, have exhumed human belongings. Evidently Mazama has erupted so recently that primitive people were included among the forms of life which the roaring giant put to death in its destructive periods. Archeologists have come upon sandals buried in Mount Mazama pumice near Bend. At Fort Rock Cave, near Newberry Crater, nearly a hundred of these were found, also buried in pumice but evidently much older than those found at Bend, according to the Carbon 14 content.

Since it seems that Mazama once stood at a much loftier elevation, it is interesting to speculate what happened to the tremendous amount of material which composed its upper heights. In the closing years of the last glacial age, the Cascade Mountains, including Mount Mazama, were shrouded by ice. As the ice dwindled, eruption of ash and pumice from Mazama coated the frozen countryside, as if to hasten the melting of the icy covering and to usher in a new landscape for this part of the Pacific Northwest.

The next act of this awakening giant was to rupture the rocky roof which before had sealed off the seething materials in the lower chamber. Indians in the vicinity fled in panic, along with frightened animals. The rumbling and shaking ground gave warning of what was to come. At first the eruptions were fairly mild, only sand-like particles being ejected. But finally the particles grew larger, the roaring increased, and—for a hundred miles east and northeast of the volcano—ashes showered down on the plateau. Smoke probably obscured much of the volcanic activity in the daytime but there must have been brilliant sunsets when the volcanic dust floated in the air at sundown; and at night, the fiery arcs of upthrown material were likely visible for miles.

The roaring ejection of ashes and associated materials continued for several weeks; then eruption stopped. When the air had cleared, the surrounding country had a new and fearful appearance. Ashes had settled over an area thousands of square miles in extent. On the mountain itself, fifty feet of pumice remained. At Bend, seventy miles from Mazama, six inches of volcanic matter covered the ground. The forests growing on the sides of the peak had been consumed—now only charred stumps remained. Since radioactive carbon remaining in burned wood determines its age, it was easy to show by tests on charred stumps of Mazama that they were consumed by fire, 6500 years ago.

Eruption again followed a period of calm, more terrible than before. It sent an avalanche-like wave of red-hot pumice down the Rogue River for thirty-five miles. Another stream of this material poured out over the plateau as far as Chemult. The flow contained large blocks of pumice which exploded like bombs. Diamond Lake was crossed by yet another stream which spilled into the North Umpqua canyon. Canyons on the side of the mountains which had been cut by glaciers were filled with fiery material two to three hundred feet deep. From the sky at night the area would have looked like a great fiery octopus.

After the last explosion and after the wind had swept the air clean of the dust and smoke, the volcanic peak looked vastly different. Its ice-clad top was gone and its caldera was gigantic. It has been estimated that, to form this crater, seventeen cubic miles of mountain were destroyed.

Following a long period of inactivity the magma remaining in the reservoir gained strength. One day it forced open the caldera floor. A lake of lava soon formed. After a period of flow, some explosions occurred which threw out thicker material around the vent and these formed a small cone, the miniature volcano of Wizard Island. This action has also been dated. The oldest trees on the island indicate that this last eruption of Mazama occurred about one thousand years ago. Gas vents and hot springs in the vicinity of volcanoes show the presence of magma, the name given to underground lava. There are no vents or springs about Mazama. Even so, this old volcano may one day repeat itself.

Dutton Cliff tells a portion of Mazama's story. There layers of tuff—a rock composed of bedded ash—are clearly seen (Photo No. 33). This indicates

Photo No. 33   National Park Service

Dutton Cliff tells a portion of Mount Mazama's story. Note the succession of layers of volcanic materials on the cliff's face. The light-colored layers are finer stratified materials called tuff—a rock composed of bedded ash. Lovely Phantom Ship rises from Crater Lake's shadowed waters.

that sometimes molten rock flowed over the rim and down the sides of the volcano, and sometimes only dust and cinders.

That the elements are busily at work on the crater walls is evident in the rock fragments composing several rock slides, or talus slopes, that have developed from the top of the rim to the water's edge. Particle by particle, the agents of heat, cold, and running water are plucking away at the margin of the lake. Possibly in some future age a portion of

[153]

the rim will become sufficiently lowered by this type of erosion to drain a part of the water in Crater Lake.

Newberry Crater

The scenic wonderland of Oregon is renowned for its unique and sometimes spectacular volcanic phenomena. In one place it is the overwhelming size, the immensity of the explosive event, which amazes the observer. In another, it is the curious way in which the outpouring of lava developed in form or direction which stirs the imagination.

Newberry Crater must rank as spectacular. You can see it by driving for half an hour east, off the junction of U. S. Highway 97, only twenty-four miles from Bend. In so doing you can imagine the thoughts which entered the mind of Peter Skene Ogden, on October 16, 1826, when he looked down for the first time at what is one of the world's largest craters. It is fitting that such a superb crater should bear the name of a geologist—Dr. John S. Newberry, who accompanied the Williamson expedition which explored central Oregon in 1855.

From the junction, at elevation 4200 feet, the climb reaches 6371 feet at the crater. The incline up which the highway progresses is a shield volcano four thousand feet thick at its top and twenty miles in diameter. Nature varied the consistency of the fluid rock with which it flooded this area; basalt and rhyolite, now solidified in well-defined layers, rose at intervals from the earth's interior.

To the imaginative, this immense caldera which is Newberry Crater can suggest the terrifying scene in ancient times when this was a fiery lake of exploding gases and seething stone—finally settling into its rumbling depths. Here, as well as at every turn of the highway and on every mountain trail, the scenic geology of the Pacific Northwest becomes a dramatic story.

When the fearful eruptions at Newberry Crater subsided and the floor solidified, water collected in the caldera and, for a time, occupied the newly-formed crater. Then came more activity, but not enough to liquefy the entire crater into its original fury. Small craters, forming a north-south line across the middle, burst into life a short time, then died. The large single lake now became two, East and Paulina, as they are seen today. East Lake, fed by numerous mineral springs, has no inlet or outlet. Paulina Lake overflows in a low portion of the west rim into Paulina Creek, which in turn joins the East Fork of the Deschutes River. Paulina Creek leaps down the sides of this volcanic mountain in several waterfalls. Most scenic of these features is Paulina Falls, one hundred feet high, and just a short distance west of the lake.

The damaged west walls of Newberry Crater limit the amount of water it can hold. A part of the north rim is obscured by mile-wide lava, which flowed that direction, possibly breaking the crater rim and carrying it away. One, however, can still perceive the great proportions of this volcano because three fourths of the rim are still intact.

The most interesting episode among the concluding years of volcanic time was a rupture of the inner wall of the Newberry Crater from which volcanic glass flowed down in cataracts of glowing obsidian. When cooled, the extremely rough mass of rock extended three miles to the crater floor and at one place was nearly a mile wide.

The grandeur of the Newberry Crater country can best be discovered on a trail leading to Paulina Peak, from the west end of Paulina Lake. The three-mile climb is steep but, from its summit, Newberry Crater and its fascinating features appear spread out below in massive proportions. From this point and this height, most of central Oregon is visible— and silence is all around. There is something about broken lava rock, the ghostly shades on white pine bark, and the rocky rim of the empty, lifeless crater far below, that wakens spirits of ages past.

Fort Rock

So much of the Northwest has a youthful topography that it is easy to fall into general terms when describing it. There are some features, however, like Fort Rock, whose origin goes back to earlier times. This rock is an almost vertical, circular escarpment standing alone on the fairly level plateau in central Oregon. It can be reached from State Highway 31, near Silver Lake, or east from Horse Ranch (Photos Nos. 34 and 35). From a distance this formation appears like sedimentary bedding, but it is actually igneous agglomerate, or pieces of various-sized, angular lava cemented together. Its roughly-circular shape has an opening on its southern perimeter, permitting entry into a huge enclosure surrounded by rock walls, 325 feet above the earth floor, which would, as its name implies, serve as an excellent fort.

Inside, Fort Rock shows itself to be a very old volcano that has been greatly subdued by erosion. Its south side has entirely collapsed. Today this rock is considered only a remnant in comparison with volcanoes like the Three Sisters, yet it is still an impressive landmark—still defying the elements which seek to destroy it.

Photo No. 34 *above:* Fort Rock, a volcanic survivor of the giant upheaval that took place centuries ago in central Oregon's high plateau region. Observe the work of erosion on the crater walls and the features of the surrounding land, once a lake bottom.

Photo No. 35 *below:* Closer view of a portion of a Fort Rock wall. Fragmental lava composition of the formation is noticeable.

The character of the earth around Fort Rock reveals that, at one time, probably in the Pleistocene Period, lake water surrounded it. With the collapse of one side, waves surged through the opening, battering the walls and carrying sediment into the rocky crater. Waves beating against the outer walls explain their upright position; also the absence of loose material, commonly found on the outer slopes of volcanoes. All this was picked up and carried away.

According to Phil F. Brogan, Northwest geologist, these waves spread east to Christmas Lake, covering the area to a depth of some two hundred feet; and, providing ancient tribes lived at that time in nearby Cow Cave—the oldest known habitation of man in Oregon—they viewed a spectacular sight: steam boiling from the ancient lake and lava-like mud spouting from a central vent. Eventually the lake disappeared, after shaping the giant amphitheater.

This spectacular landmark is to be developed as a state park, with a road leading into the area from the village of Fort Rock. The story of the rock will be outlined on a roadway sign.

The Three Sisters

The Three Sisters area, east of Eugene, Oregon, on U. S. Highway 126, is a volcanic region containing a store of information for the geologist, and spectacular scenery for the tourist. Although the major volcanoes—which stand in a north-south line in the Pacific Coast states — have perhaps gained more popularity, there are many others, including those in the Three Sisters group, which are equally beautiful and interesting historically.

On a drive east from Eugene, two phases of mountain building in Oregon show clearly. The western Cascades were first upfolded. Previously there were no mountains here to catch the moisture of the winds from the Pacific Ocean. Because of the moist climate, the John Day country at that time grew redwood trees, which are now preserved as fossils and proof of these interesting conditions. Early in the Pliocene, the moisture supply for these water-loving trees was cut off by the western-rising Cascade Mountains. Geologists now class as mature, Oregon's western Cascades, because they have been much lowered and rounded by ages of erosion.

Farther east, and somewhat later, there was built a group of volcanoes consisting of basalt and basaltic andesite rock. These are now called the Three Sisters. This became a most rugged region, one changed by the growth of new peaks and a variety of volcanic displays. The rugged region of the Sisters includes the so-called family peaks of Little Brother, Husband, and Wife; and two others, Sphinx and Broken Top.

During the Pleistocene, the Middle and South Sisters erupted, and minor cones nearby came into being. Showers of pumice, basaltic lava and scoria and even massive flows belched from earth-vents, chiefly from the Belknap Crater near McKenzie Pass. Volcanism has persisted here even into recent times. It is said that nowhere else in the High Cascades has more volcanic activity occurred in the last millennium. Taken as a whole, the volcanic history of the Three Sisters was much like that of the Crater Lake region and parts of the Cascade Range farther south.

What do the Oregon High Cascades hold today? Most noticeable of all, at least from a distance, are the massive ice-capped cones of the major Three Sisters Peaks and the spectacular glacial scenery. There are seventeen glaciers still surviving; some lakes dammed by moraines and others cut by ice—all scattered at the feet of these imposing peaks. There are barren layers of lava, only a few centuries old, covering almost a hundred square miles. Here, also, are fresh obsidian and youthful cinder cones.

For detailed study of volcanoes, this is the place to visit. Some of the older volcanoes in the Three Sisters group have been so severely eroded that their central cores, the places where the melted rock rose in volcanic throats, are clearly visible. Also in evidence are lavas that left volcanoes by side vents, now hardened into dikes and exposed by the down-cutting of the mountainsides.

Photograph No. 36 shows the ruggedness of the Three Sisters area in Oregon, as well as the severe erosion which this region has undergone. The glacial cirque on the peak in the foreground may have enlarged a crater. Possibly this circular pit was once continuously rimmed with rock and later its lower side opened by a glacier. A glacier occupies this interesting feature today. In fact, glaciers are constantly at work on these peaks, exposing their volcanic character.

Future of the Cascades

The period of time in which the volcanoes of the Cascades were erected was an age of construction. Crust disturbances had warped this region into a mountainous area, and warping movements had been accompanied by a great deal of volcanism, all climaxed by the formation of the Cascade volcanoes.

Photo No. 36   *Oregon State Highway Commission*

Three Sisters Peaks in Oregon, once active volcanoes, are now being attacked by glaciers. In the foreground crater, snow and rock have created what appears to be a human face. Some of the older volcanoes in the Three Sisters group have been so severely eroded that their central cores are clearly visible.

Evidence today in the form of fumeroles and hot springs, that still survive in some volcanoes, points to declining volcanic energy. Volcanism generally is dying, and there is no evidence of rejuvenation. Forces of destruction have replaced those of construction, and the Cascade Mountains with their snow-capped volcanoes are now at the mercy of erosion. Countless streams and rivers are attacking the mountainsides. Bit by bit, the rock is being loosened and carried to the Pacific Ocean—the destination in time for all elevated land west of the Continental Divide.

Since the activities of volcanoes are unpredictable, geologists cannot give assurance that the quiet which now prevails will not be broken by new eruptions. Vesuvius had not erupted for six hundred years when it exploded into action. Should Pacific Northwest volcanoes again erupt, those who witness the spectacle will doubtless notice some change in the events that follow. Since the volcanoes on the Cascade Mountains are now all plugged with solidified rock, old craters there will probably not be activated. Explosions will be more apt to break out of the sides of existing volcanoes, in areas which have been deeply eroded. Lava will flow down the valleys for about ten miles. Most damage by any future volcanic eruption will be suffered by cities and towns through the showers of ashes.

Columbia Plateau—A Lava Flood

On the Columbia Plateau in the Pacific Northwest are vast solidified outpourings of once-liquid rock. This plateau extends from the Cascade Mountains in Washington and Oregon to some points as far east as the Rockies. Its northern border is roughly the northward bend of the Columbia River and its southern edge is deep in Oregon, south of the Columbia. Because of the complexities of some of the mountain structures in eastern Oregon, the boundaries of the basalt plateau in this state have not been accurately defined. This vast plateau of once-liquid rock—now in some places deeply cut by erosion—is two hundred thousand square miles in area and contains an estimated twenty-four thousand cubic miles of basalt, a brown-to-black, finely-grained igneous rock. A drive across this deposit offers a spectacular sight (Photos Nos. 37 and 38).

Much is known about the Columbia Plateau but there is still much to be learned. It has been visited by hundreds of flows, some only a few feet thick,

Photo No. 37   *Washington State Advertising Commission*

This is typical coulee country of eastern Washington, with flows of lava visible along the highway and on distant cliffs. Note the lines defining individual flows and the talus rubble collecting at the base of the basalt cliffs.

others more than seven hundred. According to geologists, the flows are at least five thousand feet thick in the middle of the field. Something of the thickness and steepness of the exposed flows is observable at many places along the Columbia River Highway, where water falling 620 feet down a basalt cliff helps the eye to adjust to nature's often great dimensions (Photo No. 39).

There is proof that considerable time elapsed between some of the periods of flowing **rock** liquids.

Photo No. 38   *Washington State Advertising Commission*

Palouse River canyon winds through picturesque lava flows, the result of centuries of entrenchment through countless flows. The scene here is just below the falls. A total of 200,000 square miles in Washington and Oregon is covered by many flows of basalt lava.

Visitors exploring on foot will be certain to notice the bedded character of the many layers of basalt. Separating some of them are thin layers of soil formed by weathering of the rock below. The soil

Photo No. 39   *Oregon State Highway Commission*

Multnomah Falls on the Columbia River Highway, in Oregon, hurtles 620 feet down a precipitous basalt cliff. The steepness of exposed flows of once-liquid rock is observable at many places along this scenic highway.

is now highly baked but occasionally charred bits of roots and wood can be pried loose, conclusive evidence that there was not always a close succession of lava flows over the land and also that plant life grew in the soil formed in the intervals between lava flows. Under a microscope, particles of soil also include the remains of tiny marine organisms, showing that lakes once occupied shallows in the stony surface of the hardened lava.

A strange sight is Grand Coulee, a dry canyon in the sun-baked and wind-swept rock of the Columbia Plateau. Its upper floor opens in the basalt fifteen hundred feet above the Columbia River, beyond Coulee Dam. From there, continuing almost due south for fifty miles, it looks as if a giant tool had reamed out a trench for draining water away in some historic flood. This trench is a thousand feet deep and nearly a mile wide. On its floor are potholes, a hundred feet deep, made by water-turned rocks. Along its channel lie ancient river bars which reach two hundred feet in depth. Perpendicular, forbidding walls of weather-stained and algae-covered basalt outline this trench when viewed from the rims —or from U. S. Highway No. 2, which crosses it near Coulee City.

This great trough is an ancient watercourse. During glacial times a lobe, or tongue of ice, extending from polar regions, plowed its way down the Okanogan Valley and into and beyond the Columbia River. The ice was great enough in volume and in depth to dam the Columbia. Because of gravity, unconfined water seeks new drainage avenues. The Columbia, which ordinarily flowed in the Big Bend around the northwest bulge of the Columbia basalt, was no exception. Dammed at the northern rim of the basalt, it now took off across it to the south.

The Columbia, then, eroded that spectacular channel now called Grand Coulee. However, this was not accomplished with the ordinary amount of water at its disposal. It was an angry and swollen Columbia, driven by many times its usual volume of water, which carved its way into hard basalt for fifty miles and then spread out over the Quincy Basin before it again drained into its former channel at the southern arc of the Big Bend. What caused such a quantity of water is still argued. Most scientists who have studied the region agree that the ice dam which started it all was a temporary feature and that Grand Coulee was excavated in a comparatively short time. It seems likely that the flood water was the result of a rather drastic climatic change at the close of the Pleistocene Age. Lying to the north of the Columbia drainage, ice of great thickness had accumulated for centuries, no doubt for thousands of years. Now in the warmth of a climatic change, this turned to water which filled existing channels and even spread out over flat lands in eastern Washington. All evidence indicates that a large and lingering ice dam lay across the Columbia channel — the most important river in the region—and it in turn gave new direction to the water which was shifted abruptly south by it. The result was Grand Coulee, one of the world's best examples of river erosion.

Because of its size, one picture cannot do justice to the Columbia Plateau, nor can several. Photograph No. 40 shows Dry Falls, a favorite spot in the coulee for picture taking. At Dry Falls, where many of the layers of lava are presently distinct, glacial runoff water descended over a fall ranked among the greatest in the world. Its semicircular rim saw the passage of many cubic miles of water each day. Its plunge-pool of similar shape contained one of

Photo No. 40   *Washington State Advertising Commission*

Dry Falls in Grand Coulee in Washington, a temporary channel occupied by the
Columbia River when that great stream was dammed by glacial ice. Note the plunge
pool in the foreground and on the east river bank on the horizon—also the layered lava
in the background.

the wildest maelstroms of water known to science.
Dry Falls is 400 feet high; whereas Niagara, in New
York, is only 167; and Victoria, in Africa, 343.
Around the rim of prehistoric Dry Falls there is a
three-mile walk for observing, at the foot of the
cliffs, the plunge-pools, now lakes, over which the
water fell.

Steamboat Rock, in the upper portion of Grand
Coulee, was caused by the widening of the coulee
from waterfalls which worked around this rock
until it became an island in the gorge (Photo No.
41). It is two miles long, three-fourths of a mile
wide, and nine hundred feet high. Once an island, it

Photo No. 41   *Washington State Advertising Commission*

Steamboat Rock, a plateau remnant in the channel of Grand Coulee. Cut by a
rampaging Columbia River at the close of the glacial period, this coulee is one of the
greatest examples of river erosion in the world.

is again an island, this time in a reservoir of quiet
water. With the building of Coulee Dam, a part of
Grand Coulee became an equalizing reservoir for irrigation water. Had it been necessary for man to ex-
cavate a basin as large as the prehistoric channel
which he has dammed for storage purposes, the effort and expense would have been prohibitive. The
Columbia did the job free of charge in an age when
no engineering supervision executed the project.

Today Grand Coulee is very quiet, except for the
passing of automobiles and the songs of birds. As

far as the eye can see, lie basalt layers whose surfaces are slowly crumbling from the weathering of the ages.

The McKenzie Lava Fields

The Columbia Plateau, built of successive flows of lava, is very old. We do not know how much time was required to flood each layer into place and, in some intervals, the amount of time required for the formation of soil and the growth of trees. The basalt which now composes one of America's great plateaus was erupted in the Miocene period, thirty million years ago. By using modern methods of observation we can be sure that much time has elapsed since the last flow here occurred. Much of the plateau surface is crumbled, weather beaten, and covered with lichens.

Several places in the Northwest have more recent lava deposits. The rock of the McKenzie Lava Fields is so fresh in appearance that it is said to be the latest lava flow in the continental United States. These strikingly new flows are located midway between Belknap and Sisters, Oregon. The flow area is irregularly shaped and as yet little visited. The best part to explore is between McKenzie and Santiam highways. Here great waterfalls splash grotesquely over the blackened rock.

Persons driving about the Pacific Northwest are so accustomed to the older, weathered rocks of the Cascades and elsewhere that, upon encountering the McKenzie area, they are astonished at the difference —and often bewildered. Here are layers of once-molten rock undisturbed by weathering, as fresh as the day this viscous mass writhed and twisted its way down the slope on which it lies. There is no impression of vastness, only the evidence that in this mountainous setting—perhaps coincident with the arrival of the pilgrims on our eastern shores — earth's mysterious chambers spewed molten rock out over a western landscape.

Not all of the outpoured rock in the McKenzie fields is new—only the upper layer or "frosting," yet this is the feature that is remarkable. Belknap Crater, from time to time, erupted the accumulated flows of the ages. These flows are now 3500 feet thick. The age of the older, layered foundation reaches back into the millenniums which produced the land forms of the Pacific Northwest.

Lava River Caves

The Lava River Caves—twelve miles south of Bend, Oregon, on U. S. Highway 97—have an almost incredible origin. They were created by molten lava. The interior of the cave, shown in Photo No. 42, is a smooth-walled tunnel, extending 5462 feet through solid lava one hundred feet thick. In some sections the ceiling is fifty-eight feet above the floor and, in some, it is fifty feet wide. These dimensions exceed those of the Holland Tunnel under the Hudson in New York.

In one phase of volcanic time, the lava encasing this great cave was a molten river flowing downhill into a valley. Then the top and sides of the lava stream cooled, leaving an inner core, hot, liquid— and in motion. Since the lava lay on a fairly steep gradient, terrific pressure built up within the mass. A rupture at the lower extremities of the flow allowed the still-liquid core to flow downhill and finally drain out entirely, leaving a long tunnel behind it. The lava which poured out of this unusual land form is believed to have entered the canyon of the Deschutes River.

Photo No. 42   *Oregon State Highway Commission*

Interior of a lava cave at Lava Cave State Park, near Bend, Oregon, on U. S. Highway 97. Molten lava, flowing underground, left a smooth tunnel within the cooling rock, extending 5462 feet through solid lava one hundred feet thick. Note the small solidified lava drippings on the ceiling.

A trip into Lava River Caves is an exciting experience, and a cooling one on a hot day. The visitor enters a large chamber where, in spring, are icy stalactites and s t a l a g m i t e s formed during the winter months. These last until warm June days. From the entrance room, stairs lead down to the main tunnel.

The cavern walls are surprisingly smooth, in many places as evenly proportioned as if they had been drilled with machinery. On them are part of the liquid rock remains which flowed along the cavern bore. In some places occur stalactites formed

Photo No. 43   Oregon State Highway Commission

Water, dripping here from the ceiling of the lava caves near Bend, has etched
fascinating volcanic sand gardens of miniature pinnacles, gulches and depressions, in
which lie quiet pools of water. Vertical grooves are located directly under the major
drips.

by the drip of melted rock. In others, rock shelves
extend from wall to wall of the cave, forming for
short distances a sort of horizontal partition in the
tunnel. These shelves represent the various levels of
the underground river of lava, possibly in the later
stages of its flow when the tunnel was not entirely
full of molten rock.

Volcanic sand covers much of the floor. At one
point, dripping water has eroded the sand into miniature sand gardens of pinnacles, gulches, and depressions, in which lie quiet pools of water (Photo
No. 43).

Photo No. 44

Roadside view of columnar structure in Columbia basalt near Spokane, Washington. Usually seen in vertical position, these structures form part of the top layers of lava which once spilled over thousands of square miles in the Northwest.

Columnar Structure

Columbia Plateau basalt has one especially notable feature—its columns are so symmetrical that they could conceivably be removed intact and used in building construction (Photo No. 44). These columnar structures form part of the top layers of lava which once spilled over thousands of square miles in the Northwest. At that time melted rock flowed freely, sealing the landscape beneath it. When the flow finally stopped and the fiery sea cooled, the rock often contracted and cracked much as mud does in places of drought. Deep crevices, extending into the rock, cracked these columns. Besides furnishing important clues to the extent of long-ago eruptions, the columns add interest and beauty to the landscape.

Craters of the Moon

One of the latest eruptions—with its young volcanic substances—can be seen at Craters of the Moon in the central part of Idaho. Although volcanic activity continued intermittently during at least three prehistoric epochs at Craters of the Moon, the final activity likely ceased somewhere within the last five hundred years.

Located within this National Monument there is what geologists call a Great Rift—something one might expect in a volcanic region. Such a rift is a zone of weakness or series of fissures through which pressured lava might erupt under certain conditions. It is an interesting phenomenon because along it occurred practically every kind of volcanic activity. Nature never performed violently here; on the contrary, the landscape pattern is the result of quiet flows and sputtering volcanism.

A variety of volcanic forms will be seen here where the craters and related features are spread over 48,000 acres. Much of this area is hard on shoes because some of the lava is so fresh that the clinker-like cinders are quite sharp. However, plenty of smoother surfaces can be selected for easy walking.

Perhaps the most arresting features of these craters are the cinder cones, chief among which is Big Cinder Butte, rising about eight hundred feet above its base. This small volcano ranks among the world's few cinder cones of pure basalt. It was formed from gas-filled basalt particles showered out in a kind of froth by the volcano. When hardened, the particles and pebble-sized pieces rolling down all sides of the

Photo No. 45

National Park Service

Looking down into one of the thirty-five cinder cones at Craters of the Moon Monument, in south central Idaho. Upon the sides of the crater can be seen the cinder materials lying in roughly-layered positions.

volcano formed a symmetrical cone. Craters of the Moon has thirty-five of these cinder cones to be explored (Photo No. 45).

The lava-dome type of volcano is also represented here. Quiet lava flowing from a crack in the earth produces these domes that are low and rounded, often resembling thick lumberjack pancakes. The spatter cones are different. They are formed by boiling, fudge-like blobs of lava which are ejected from the crater, then hardened in irregular masses

Photo No. 46

National Park Service

The aa type of lava flow at Craters of the Moon National Monument in south central Idaho. This lava has a rough, jumbled appearance—and is very hard on shoes. The fresh look of this lava indicates quite recent eruption in this area.

on the crater's sides. In these craters the vents are smaller than in most volcanoes and the inside tapers away from the vent much as a funnel placed upside down.

The flows of lava, in Idaho's Craters of the Moon, moved quietly away from earth vents to spread helter-skelter over the land, and a queer land it is. The flows are in such topsy-turvy arrangement that it seems as if there had been a battle among them over the route which each would take.

Photo No. 47   *Idaho Department of Highways*

This is the pahoehoe type of lava, also at Craters of the Moon. In contrast to the aa, pahoehoe lava has a smooth, glistening surface. Here it has taken on a ropy form.

In the main, there are two kinds of lava flows recognized by geologists and both appear in this region. The aa (pronounced ah-ah) type is the kind that is hard on shoe leather. It is sharp, broken and irregular and its flow is apt to be massive and shapeless (Photo No. 46). A second kind, the pahoehoe (pronounced pah-hoe-ay-hoe-ay) is smoother, frequently ropy and twisted somewhat like taffy. Often pahoehoe flows assume regular patterns and the curving ropes take on pleasing symmetry (Photo No. 47). Both words — aa and pahoehoe — are Hawaiian.

Besides the cones and lava flows there are many other volcanic items within the twelve-mile length of the monument. The lava "bombs" are pieces of lava with a teardrop shape and a rather slender tail. These are formed when lumps of lava are thrown into the air and hardened sufficiently to retain their approximate shape when they strike the ground. "Bombs" vary in size from less than an inch to large pieces that a man could not move.

There are tree molds also in this area where molten lava flowed around the trunks of standing trees. Since these were engulfed at various levels, doubtless considerable time elapsed between some periods of this volcanic activity. Along the Great Rift occur pit craters where the surface of lava collapsed as the flow subsided. Water is often found in these, since they served as catch-basins for the water which percolates through the network of crevices throughout the broken area. Finally, the area contains lava caves, tubes, and natural bridges.

Dome Volcanoes

Generally speaking, there are two types of volcanoes. One is known as the lava dome, mentioned earlier. This type of volcano builds a great sloping dome or shield of rock from the spreading flow sent out through the central vent. In the lava dome, each layer of lava rarely exceeds twenty-five feet in thickness and, as eruptions continue, fissures open in the edges of the dome. In time, these fissures rob the volcano of its power to erupt through its original opening. The magma cannot rise sufficiently in the central vent to add more height to the volcano. At this point the volcano grows in diameter only.

In the Pacific Ocean, enormous lava domes have built up from the ocean floor. When, ages ago, these rose above sea level, a chain of tropic islands was formed—the islands of Hawaii. There, pineapples and sugar cane flourish in soil weathered from the brownish lava.

The Hawaiian Islands are literally dotted with the shells of dead craters, among which are some still in the prime of volcanic activity. Kilauea, whose top is only 4088 feet above sea level, is not a mountain at all, but a boiling caldron on a high plain. Here red, molten rock rises and falls in an angry vent. Mauna Loa, a true volcano, rises 13,680 feet above the tropic Pacific Ocean, often splitting its sides and radiating smoking streams of lava like the spokes of a wheel.

Nowhere in the fifty states of the Union, except in the Hawaiian Islands, can one stand on the crater rim of an active volcano to view the molten convulsions below. One of the first to record his impressions of such a visit was Admiral Charles Wilkes. In 1840, he wrote, "I can never hope again to witness such a sublime scene. The very idea of standing on the summit of one of the highest peaks in the midst of this vast ocean, in close proximity to a precipice of profound depth, overhanging an immense crater 'outrageous as a sea' with molten rock, would have been exciting even to a strong man; but the sensation was overpowering to one already exhausted by breathing the rarefied air and toiling over the lava which this huge caldron must have vomited forth in quantities sufficient to form a dome sixty miles in diameter and nearly three miles in height."

In the Atlantic Ocean lies Iceland, the largest lava flow of modern times. Beneath the deep ice cap there may be twenty or thirty active volcanoes. Many domes of lava can be said to have created Iceland.

Composite Volcanoes

A second type of volcano is known as the composite. This is the kind that comes to mind when volcanoes make the news. The composite takes shape when rock fragments, ashes, and even lava itself, fall in a circular pile around the vent after having been thrown upward by explosive action. Although the composite may have lava flowing from its side fissures, the material ejected from its central crater predominates. The resulting mountain has wonderful symmetry and upon its sides lies eternal snow. Composite volcanoes are the sentinels of the heights that they occupy. Many, like Vesuvius in Italy, Fujiyama (more correctly Fuji-mo-Yama) in Japan, and Rainier in western Washington, rise over ten thousand feet above sea level. All Pacific Northwest volcanoes are of the composite variety—all have on their sides stratified lava flows, ashes, and other blown-out material.

The crustal skin of the earth possibly rests on a molten interior, yet this cannot be verified. However, earthquake waves recorded on seismographs indicate that at a great depth there is a change in the make-up of the rocky crust. The material below may or may not be molten rock but it is evident that large quantities of this material feed volcanoes often active for long periods. If molten lava is present below, it will seek the weakest point to blow out the volcano-forming material. This underground lava, or magma, loaded with gas and heat, is under pressure and searching for an outlet. Weaknesses in the earth occur where rock layers have been arched and broken upward into mountain masses. That is why most volcanoes are located in mountain regions.

Like the earthquake, the volcano can stage large surprises. Katmai, a volcano on Kodiak Island in Alaska, had remained quiet so long that it was thought to have died. However, on June 6, 1912, it startled the world, particularly Alaska, by blowing its top off, leaving a crater three miles in diameter and 3700 feet deep. The material blown into the air was chiefly dust. A foot of it settled on everything at Kodiak Island and, on the Alaska mainland, it was sixty hours before the sun was visible. Most of the country received deposits of Katmai's dust.

The Alaskan landscape has seen much disturbance created by its explosive volcanoes. Some of these have violent histories; some seem to have become dormant or extinct; others, like Paulof, intermittently puff black ashes and steam. The Aleutian Islands, a chain of eighty large volcanoes and scores of smaller craters, extend spear-like, twelve hundred miles west from the Alaska Peninsula into the north Pacific Ocean. Among these crater islands, Shishaldin, nearly ten thousand feet high, is the tallest.

Hot Springs

Much less awesome, but still connected with volcanism, are hot springs, which, through their ability to dissolve minerals, often contain these minerals in solution. The presence of hot springs in volcanic areas is supposed to indicate diminishing volcanic activity. On the other hand, hot springs sometimes occur when evidence of volcanic activity is absent. At Hot Springs and at Quinn's, both in Western Montana, the waters flow in an area where sedimentary rock predominates. Sol Duc Hot Springs in the Olympic National Park, in Washington, occurs in an area of some igneous rock but no volcanoes. The "Washington Guide" tells of an Indian legend in which "two dragons, Sol Duc and Elwha, engaged in bitter conflict. As neither could subdue the other, they crept back to their caverns, sealed the entrances, and wept tears of mortification. Their tears form the Sol Duc and Olympic hot springs." Like today's geologists, the Indians of long ago felt the need for explaining strange phenomena.

The hot water at Lakeview, on U. S. Highway 395, in central Oregon, may have some connection with volcanic activity. However, Ohanapecosh Hot Springs is definitely related to volcanism, lying as it does at the foot of Mount Rainier in the southeast corner of the Mount Rainier National Park in Washington.

Some kind of volcanism has always been part of the earth's landscape. Though several areas, such as Mexico's Pericutin, are experiencing their first rumble of volcano building, there are other areas with volcanoes so old that erosion has reduced them to the ground level from which they started building. Diamonds found in the Kimberley area of Africa are dug from hard clay in the necks of old volcanoes that are now leveled by erosion and long since devoid of their once-fiery character. Four hundred and fifty of the world's volcanoes have erupted in the short span of historical time. Many are dormant; some have been declared dead. During geologic time our evolving landscape has seen thousands of volcanoes erupt for a time—then become part of the mountain range which gave them birth, subject to the same erosion as their neighbors.

The age of a volcano, and how recently it erupted, can be determined in several ways, but its degree of weathering is the best yardstick. Old volcanoes bear great weathering scars and their sides are gouged by deep valleys—the work of streams and glaciers. These volcanoes are also lower, their heights whittled down by harsh erosion. Even though a volcano has not erupted during historical time, it may be classed as dormant if the ashes and lava thrown out by it have been only moderately eroded.

Chapter 8

RIVERS OF THE NORTHWEST

Rivers and their tributaries lower all landscapes. They destroy the picturesque hills and mountains and leave only empty plains. The Pacific Northwest owes most of its beauty to its youth—its rivers have not yet succeeded in leveling much of the rugged terrain. Its residents still have a wealth of river-lore close at hand. And the rivers, with their varying courses and recreational provisions, constantly lure both the explorer and the vacationer.

The Columbia River

Headwaters of the Columbia, the great River of the West, is Columbia Lake in the Canadian Rockies of British Columbia. When the water flowing out of Columbia Lake has finished its journey at the Pacific Ocean, it has traveled more than one thousand miles. Aided by its tributaries, the Columbia has by that time accumulated a drainage area of 259,000 square miles and reached the status of the second largest river on this continent. Thousands of streams and several other large rivers join the Columbia to give it a flow at its mouth eight times that of the Colorado River at Yuma and twice that of the Nile at Aswan. The Columbia is potentially a power giant. More power can be developed along its channel than along that of any other river in America.

Its waters reach the ocean after a much longer journey than seems necessary. From Columbia Lake, the river heads northwest for two hundred miles. When it arrives at the northern end of the Selkirk Range—behind whose eastern sides it has flowed—it changes its direction to flow southward for 270 miles along the western flanks of these mountains. On leaving the Selkirks it has 170 miles to go in Canada. One hundred and thirty miles of this distance is occupied by the Upper and Lower Arrow Lakes, rather narrow bodies of water that are evidently the work of a glacier. Between Arrow Lakes and the International Boundary, two major tributaries join the Columbia: the Kootenai, which drains a large area in Canada and Idaho; and the Clark Fork, which heads in the Rocky Mountains and flows across western Montana and Idaho.

Just after crossing the boundary, the Columbia enters the quiet waters of the reservoir behind Grand Coulee Dam. This reservoir, now called Lake Roosevelt, is 150 miles long. It lies in the old Columbia Valley, with its waters extending into the flooded tributary valleys and its sides skirted by green pines and semi-open hillsides typical of eastern Washington. The lake's potentials of cruising, swimming, fishing, and camping destine it to become a resort center.

After producing 1,944,000 kilowatts of power at Coulee Dam, the Columbia continues its great bend around the Columbia Plateau. A short distance south of Pasco it turns, heading directly west toward the ocean. First, however, it must move the turbines at McNary, The Dalles and Bonneville dams, pass through the gorge which it has cut in the Cascades, and swing northward around the upper end

Photo No. 48   *Oregon State Highway Commission*

Waters of the Columbia River once roared over a cleft in the volcanic-like river bed to form Celilo Falls near The Dalles, Oregon. This view shows the extent of the falls where Indians speared and netted fish from the rocks before the erection of the dam.

of Oregon's coast range. Only then is it free to rush on to the sea. (Photo No. 48).

Assigning an age to the Columbia River is difficult. It has few signs of maturity or old age, yet some of the rock with which it is associated indicates that the Columbia has been at work for a very long time. In some places the bed of the Columbia appears to have been just recently started. In others the river has spread out in a braided channel as if to begin the meandering of maturity, only to collect its water and plunge through a narrow gorge. In general, though, the Columbia should be considered youthful.

Not always has the Columbia reached the ocean down the channel it uses today. We can be sure that the Big Bend in Washington was not formerly a part of its pattern. Instead, upon entering what is now American soil in the northeast corner of Washington, the river flowed southeastward toward the Columbia River Gorge and the sea. The kind of topography through which the early river traveled cannot be described accurately. There are, however, a few clues to the appearance of the country at that time.

The Big Bend of the Columbia was caused by the lava flow which in Miocene time poured out of the earth and flowed northward, pushing the Columbia in a great arc along its northern edge. Except for a few places where the river cuts across portions of the basalt, the Columbia today flows between the lava and the older rock of the Okanogan Highlands and the Cascade Mountains. Not all earth features were engulfed by the lava. For instance, Steptoe Butte—a landmark near Steptoe, in the Palouse country of southeast Washington — was only surrounded by the lava flow. These meager clues suggest that the early Columbia flowed through a low rolling country, probably one considerably eroded by a network of tributary streams.

When the immense lava flow on the Columbia Plateau was in the making, the river was in great peril. Surely for a time no water flowed in the lower reaches of the river. Part of the channel was likely clogged with lava, but that made little difference because there was little water to form a river; water meeting the hot lava would have turned to steam. When the lava flood subsided, the Columbia could no

Photo No. 49   *Walla Walla District, Corps of Engineers*

As rivers go, the Columbia is young, yet its mighty waters were already flowing when these great layered cliffs in the background were being formed. Here a barge and tug head upstream on this famous River of the West—now a power giant.

longer choose the shortest route across Washington to the ocean. Now it had to seek a channel along the northern boundary of the newly-arrived lava (Photo No. 49).

In its fascinating history, the Columbia has known two extremes—first the heat of scorching lava that almost erased it, then the cold of the Ice Age that partly congealed its water and scoured its sides as the ice slid over them. During the close of this age, ice dammed the river; and the melt water, swollen to flood proportions, raced over the basalt to cut Grand Coulee.

It seems that the Columbia has often met hazards threatening its peaceful passage to the sea. It survived the battle with northern ice in the Pleistocene after it had been pushed from its channel by the fiery lava of the Miocene. Because of the rapidity

Union Pacific

The Columbia was pushed from its course by the rush of molten lava during the Miocene Age. In some places—like Wallula Gap, Washington, shown here—it cut through portions of the lava. The slightly tilted layers of basalt are seen on both banks.

with which the molten rock spread over the interior of Washington, the Columbia could not keep pace. Yet, in some places, it won—it cut through portions of the lava. This probably happened in places where river water ponded. Finding no gradient around the edges of the basalt, water ran over it, in time cutting its way through. Such a place is at Wallula Gap in Horse Heaven Hills, where the river has worn a passage in stubborn basalt (Photo No. 50).

Since its deposition, the basalt in eastern Washington, and elsewhere, has been locally uplifted. Horse Heaven Hills country is an example of this. Here the Columbia was forced to dig its bed at the same rate as uplift, or be forced to find still another channel. Next, it had to gouge a gateway through the Cascade Mountains.

Two fine highways pass through the Columbia Gorge—one on the Oregon bank, the other in Washington. A little exploring in the area reveals that nature, using various materials, made the gorge a formidable barrier as if to harass the river. Underneath is a foundation for all the material above, a layer of old volcanic flows and sediments. Above this are the brown Columbia basalts, layer upon layer. On top of the basalt rests a layer of gravel which in turn is covered by a lighter-colored lava. Capping all the flows and the conglomerate of intermixed

Photo No. 51   *Oregon State Highway Commission*

At sundown, west of Hood River, Oregon, Columbia River gorge elevations stand out in silhouette. Shell Rock and Wind Mountain may be seen in the distance.

materials are the ashes from recent eruptions of the local volcanoes, Mount Adams and Mount Hood. Through all this the Columbia has worn a channel. In some places, like Multnomah Falls, the gorge walls stand straight and smooth as if sawed through by mechanical means. In Photograph No. 51, are seen no vertical walls but, looking west from Hood River, one sights the lofty Cascades through which the Columbia has cut its way.

It is generally agreed that the Cascades were rising when the Columbia performed this herculean task. Was the Columbia dammed for a time by them? This is a question which geologists sometimes debate. There are those who say that it was, because the Cascade Mountains rose so rapidly. They say that the Columbia then plunged down the west side of the Cascades dam in a waterfall, or steep rapids— and, in time, as the mountain uplift slackened, the river wore away the dam to assume its present grade. In any case, the Columbia did work its way through the mountains, bearing water from a vast inland watershed and making its history unique among rivers on this continent.

We have proof that the Cascades stubbornly resisted the work of the Columbia. On the Washington side, near Carson, a lava flow once crossed the river to the Oregon side, throwing a rock dam in its path. The rock in this flow has one characteristic all its own—its grain is very fine. In time this dam was worn through. Also, near Wyeth, Oregon, a mountain of hard, diorite porphyry rose in deep-seated upheaval to challenge the river's progress. Columbia waters met this adversary head on, slicing their way through and leaving two mountains where one had been before—Wind Mountain, on the Washington side, and Shell Rock Mountain, on the Oregon.

At Cascade Locks, the Columbia turns abruptly at a right angle. Here another obstruction faced the Columbia. At this point the Eagle Creek Formation, composed of conglomerate, tilts upward, providing a plane down which great and frequent rock slides plummet to block the river. Yet, as before, the river continued to the sea. Here no cutting was necessary, the water merely changing its course by flowing around the slide.

Photo No. 52   *Oregon State Highway Commission*

The Columbia River Gorge from the Vista House atop Crown Point in Oregon. Seen through this gorge is a sweeping view of the river cutting through the lofty Cascades on its way to the sea.

There is much to see in the eighty-mile gorge of the Columbia, and lofty Crown Point is a good place from which to view it (Photo No. 52). Here, as far as the eye can travel, rolls the Columbia through the gorge of its own making. Below this point the Old Oregon Trail is now U. S. Highway 30, where to-day's traffic flows east and west. Along this route in the gorge are eight state parks and eleven water-falls.

Among geologists, the Columbia is classed as an antecedent stream because its channel was estab-lished before the uplift of the Cascades began. It is a classic example of a river maintaining its down-cutting as the land rose along its sides. Had the river not succeeded in holding its course, the mouth of the Columbia today would probably be much far-ther south; the Vista House at Crown Point would not look down on the Oregon Trail, and the state of Oregon would have a different history.

In the Columbia Basin, water from innumerable watersheds trickles, flows, and eventually surges toward the great river. The seepage from ice fields high in the Montana Rockies, the pent-up water from Idaho's subterranean rivers, the sparkling streams from the Washington Cascades, and the persistent water from the northern volcanic fields of Oregon—all seek out the Columbia.

Among these there are none more beautiful than the ones which end their journey to the river by plunging down the steep gorge walls bordering the Columbia. So frequently do falls occur along the Columbia River Highway that it is occasionally called "The Road of Falling Waters." Some of the falls are obscured by rock formations or timber, but the falls are not far away.

Eastward, the first waterfall, Latourelle, is thirty miles from Portland, on the Oregon side. Only a part of it is visible from the highway but its total drop is 224 feet. A trail leads to the pool at the base of the cliff, where there is much interesting columnar basalt. Because of the structure of the wall over which it flows, Young's River Falls, 140 feet high, looks as if it were spouting out of solid rock. Lewis and Clark noticed Mist Falls, twelve hundred feet high — and now appropriately named. Its falling waters are often turned to mist by the strong air currents of the gorge.

Something different is displayed at Wahkeena Falls, seen from the bridge which crosses Wahkeena Creek. Its waters tumble 242 feet over rock obstructions in a series of delightful drops and cascades.

Horsetail Falls barely misses the Columbia River Highway. It is carried to the bottom by a wall of basalt 208 feet high.

The Eagle Creek area, two miles east of Tanner Creek, has several falls worth visiting. One of these is a combination rock bowl and fall known as the Devil's Punch Bowl. In it, water spins and eddies before dropping into the basin below. Ghost Falls, nearby, should also be included in a trip into Eagle Creek Canyon, which is a secluded, highly scenic gorge. In the canyon wherever the Eagle Creek Formation is exposed, petrified wood and fossil leaves appear in abundance.

Multnomah Falls is the most popular and no doubt most scenic of all the falls in the Columbia Gorge. It is divided into two parts. The upper falls drops 541 feet and the lower seventy-nine. Water for this beautiful waterfall, at which many motorists stop, is supplied from Larch Mountain, an extinct volcano.

The tributary streams, which plunge down the basalt walls of the Columbia, occupy hanging valleys that enter the gorge hundreds of feet above the master stream. Their minor downcutting, no doubt due to the comparatively small amount of water which they carry, has not kept pace with the cutting of the Columbia. An immensity of time will pass before these channels will be lowered to coincide with the broad river.

Idaho Waterfalls

Waterfalls are mountain made, so Idaho has many. In 1811, Wilson Price Hunt became the first white man to see Shoshone Falls in the Snake River, now near Twin Falls. Often called the "Niagara of the West," Shoshone Falls is a grand sight in a western setting. The Snake River at this place drops 212 feet over a ledge of basalt, formed like a horseshoe and a thousand feet across. The tons of water descending over these falls thunder down in a blue torrent on which ride ribbons of foam.

The Snake River is a turbulent river. At Filer, it churns over Augur Falls in a series of strange convolutions caused by obstructions in the channel and several rocky escarpments that make the water boil and twist. All of the Snake, including its tributaries, seems to run at a rapid pace. Mesa Falls, on the North Fork of the Snake, drops 114 feet, then passes through odd erosion features before cascading over Lower Mesa Falls, sixty-five feet high, near Grandview. Here the water is concentrated in a narrower channel, giving the lower falls greater velocity.

For unusual color pictures, Jump Creek Falls, thirty miles west of Nampa, has many lovely scenes. The gorge of Jump Creek Falls changes in color according to the position of the sun. It becomes gray, blue, green, red and orange as the day advances.

River Adventures

To early trappers and explorers, rivers were avenues of travel. Lewis and Clark depended on them to float their party many of the miles to the Pacific and back. In land travel, rivers acted as direction finders because the explorers were sure that, after crossing the continental divide, westward-flowing water would lead them to the Pacific Ocean. People are still floating down rivers in canoes and in more substantial boats, shooting the rapids, and lingering in the quiet stretches to fish or camp. More and more, though, the rivers have become areas of recreation and adventure.

Probably no part of the United States has more rivers available for sports and general outdoor life than the Pacific Northwest. Just naming these rivers would be a sizable task. Northern Idaho has the emerald-green Kootenai, flowing in a canyon so deep that travel down parts of its sides is impossible. Western Montana has the Clark Fork, flowing in the valley once occupied by ancient Lake Missoula. Its channel winds through high, block-faulted mountains.

In western Washington, the Nooksack, Skagit, Stillaguamish, Skykomish and Snoqualmie, all head in the Cascade Mountains and flow toward Puget Sound. For the most part, these rivers occupy glacial troughs and their valleys are heavily timbered with giant Douglas fir, spruce and cedar. On the Olympic Peninsula, the Soleduck, Hoh, Elwha, Dose-wallips—all famed fishing waters—reach back from salt water into the dark, mysterious rain forests and into the Olympic Mountains, which compose the last remaining wilderness in America. Forest growth and underbrush are so dense in the Olympics that men have become lost by leaving a trail for only a few yards. In "Untamed Olympics," Ruby El Hult writes, "Many of the acres of this high mountain interior are still untrodden by the feet of white man, many still unmapped. Here one can travel for a month without meeting another human being or crossing one's own tracks."

Flowing northward through west-central Oregon, the Willamette and its valley cradle Eugene and Corvallis; Salem, the state capital; and Portland, the state's largest city. The Deschutes to the east, also north flowing, cuts through mountain topography of striking beauty. Still farther east, the

John Day River, by its patient excavation, has uncovered the world-famous John Day fossil beds.

On the Rogue River in southern Oregon, it is possible to float 120 miles from Grants Pass to Gold Beach through a magnificent canyon along which few roads have been made. For several days one can knife through foaming rapids — or glide along quieter water, where fishing is excellent. It is also a photographer's paradise (Photo No. 53). The sixty-four-mile round trip by boat, up the river from Gold Beach to Agness and return, provides another scenic river adventure. The route enters the heart of the Siskiyou National Forest through the colorful Rogue River canyon (Photo No. 54).

Snake River

Hell's Canyon is the roughest run of all. Only the most daring soul attempts this trip which begins at Huntington in eastern Oregon. Here you put on a life preserver, get as much boat under you as possible, then you are on your own. The building of dams on the Snake River will put an end to the longer boat runs. However, shorter trips will be possible and the ponded water in reservoirs will encourage boating in a canyon where a longer, more detailed look at the canyon walls can be enjoyed.

The best way to see a large portion of the canyon is by taking the mail boat from Lewiston, Idaho, which makes weekly trips up the river as far as Johnson's Bar. The trip requires thirteen hours, an overnight stay in the canyon, then a swift return to Lewiston the following day.

This Johnson's Bar excursion is one of the most delightful and exciting river adventures in the United States. Entry into the canyon, and bucking the rapid-flowing water, is like entering a primeval world, one

Oregon State Highway Commission

Photo No. 53 *above:* Hells Gate Canyon in the Rogue River, in southwestern Oregon. This unusually rugged region offers the landscape or fishing enthusiast a wilderness area unchanged by roads or other human developments.

Photo No. 54 *below:* Excursion boat ascending Rogue River en route from Gold Beach to Agness, Oregon—thirty-two miles upstream, into the heart of the Siskiyou National Forest through Rogue River canyon.

in which civilization has had little part. So far, the Snake River has been able to exclude roads. The gorge in which the boat threads its way is lined with rim-rock granite cliffs and basalt columns and each bend in the river unfolds a new array of somber walls, rising upward for thousands of feet. Occasionally pieces of semi-flat land are sandwiched into sharp topography. On these flatlands, cattle and sheep feed. The boat makes regular stops to deliver mail and supplies to isolated farms and miners' cabins scattered here and there en route to Johnson's Bar.

Regardless of its ruggedness, Hell's Canyon can be enjoyed quite leisurely. There is placer gold in the river, some of whose quieter eddies fill with sediments which can be worked through sluice boxes. Even though this sediment is removed during a summer of mining, the pocket, by next spring, will again be filled with sand. Fine gold can even be found in moss scraped from the canyon walls, since moss on the rocks acts as a collector of gold dust carried by water.

There is good fishing in Hell's Canyon and the fish match the immense canyon; they are huge sturgeon. They are not so numerous, though, as they were before damming of the Columbia shut off the travel of eels from the ocean. Sturgeon particularly relish eels. One old-timer says the following is the best way to catch sturgeon: Select a likely-looking eddy and a large hook. Attach the hook to a long line. Bait the hook with meat and heave it into the depths of the hole. Tie the shore end onto a sapling to which a cowbell has been attached. Set up camp. If, during the night there is a jangle of the cowbell, there will be need for some mighty pulling. Help is usually needed with a fish over eight feet in length.

Indian writings have been found at Buffalo Eddy on the Snake River, and artifacts have been discovered in a cave there. It may be—and proof seems conclusive—that a very long time ago, a group of people inhabited Hell's Canyon.

Hunting and trapping in the canyon is rough work but usually rewarding. Deer, bear, and an occasional mountain lion can be seen on the boat trips. A few men have made up to $1800 in one winter trapping coyotes—during the time when a fur neckpiece was popular among women. Coyote fur, made up, was called "Siberian wolf."

Only recently has civilization begun making inroads into Hell's Canyon. Much of it, though, will have to remain a primitive wilderness of sharp rock, great height, and cavernous depth—defying settlement or even highway penetration. To look down into this great erosion scar is to experience one of the greatest scenic thrills in the entire Northwest.

Few good roads lead to points overlooking the vast gorge. There is one, however, which rewards the traveler with a grand vista along the canyon rim. The starting point is Joseph, at the northern end of Wallowa Lake—the destination is Hat Point, a seven-thousand foot promontory on the brow of Hell's Canyon. The distance is sixty-five miles but a day should be allowed for slow driving and sufficient time to absorb the magnificent scenery. On this memorable journey—which should be made in July or August—there will be stretches of hot, treeless country, a climb up the barren walls of Imnaha Canyon, which is two to three thousand feet deep; then cool forests and the thin, crisp air of Hat Point, where a world of mountains stretches as far as the eye can see. And below are the awesome depths of the canyon, one of America's deepest gorges. More than a mile down, winds the Snake River, a silvery thread between sheer rock walls.

In this great panorama of canyon rock, four thousand feet of ancient lava flows lie one above the other, representing a time span of fifteen to twenty million years. Close observation shows stretches of bottom grade where the lava has cut completely through, exposing even older granite. At Hat Point —beyond and below—you see the sculpturing of incomprehensible time, begun in the eons before man was a part of the landscape.

About forty miles upstream from Lewiston, the Snake River is joined by the Salmon, a major Pacific Northwest river which rises and flows its entire length in one state—Idaho. The Middle Fork of the Salmon, especially its lower end, is a close cousin of the Snake. Here it drops nearly seven hundred feet in fifty miles. The Indians appropriately named the fork "The River of No Return." For those who like a run through fast water, the trip down the Middle Fork can be made with comparative safety, and accommodations are readily available. The run is a combination of riding a washboard, slalom skiing and roller coasting.

During breathing spells in this run, sixteen and eighteen-inch trout, in crystal-clear pools, can be induced to hit a fly or spoon, and camping is at its best on the clean sandbars along the river. Like the Snake, the Salmon River is a gallery of sheer cliffs, pinnacles and green timber pockets. A trip down the Middle Fork can be a wonderful river experience.

Rivers—Old and Young

When does a stream become a river? Perhaps the first settlers or explorers are to blame for their interpretation of which streams should be called rivers and which ones creeks. Some rivers are so insignificant that they can hardly be classed as rivers. In arid regions, rivers oftentimes contain water only when supplied by infrequent rainfall. On the other hand, certain creeks, which carry large volumes of water all the months of the year, would put to shame a number of streams called rivers.

Large or small, a river is usually the most important drainage channel in a given area. It is the channel to which tributaries bring water from all land sloping in its direction. Thus, rivers may be small in size, may never send water to the sea, or—like the Missouri, Columbia and Mississippi—may drain vast empires of mountain wilderness and cultivated plains. Some rivers have deep channels, some shallow. The routes of others are almost straight, while many flow in sweeping curves. There are rapids, falls, and a variety of obstacles which make rivers leap and dance, or creep sluggishly onward. The materials over which rivers flow often reveal earth history. Glacial waste and deposits of sand, gravel, and clay, along with rocks of every variety, have been laid bare by the cutting power of running water.

Like the human species, rivers show their age. They pass through a life cycle of youth, middle, and old age. A river is born on a newly-uplifted land when water collects in catch-basins or in earth cracks and moves on to lower levels. From the very beginning, a young river is an energetic worker and one of its main features is its V-shaped valley. The young river is so busy digging itself downward that it has no time to do anything about the valley walls which slope steeply down the V.

Youthful rivers are famous for their rapids and falls, and rocky bottoms. Large boulders in the river bed twist and turn the water into foaming eddies. These beginning rivers dig busily with rock fragments, not mud, for their tools. Their water is generally clear. Only during freshets do tributaries bring in muddy water. Glacial rivers are the exception, their water being continuously milky from the rock-flour fed into them by the glacier at their head.

Tributaries are also youthful, with the characteristics of a young river, but on a smaller scale. Having begun life later than the rivers to which they bring water, tributaries flow on higher ground, the rivers having a head start in cutting their channels downward. It is therefore not unusual for the tributary streams to plunge into the master river over the steep wall of a V-shaped valley.

Lakes often lie directly in the path of a young river. The land, pushed up in the form of plateaus and mountains, frequently rolls in great swells like the heaving sea, breaking into jumbled and broken hill country. Bowl-shaped depressions then fill with water which, in time, spills over the lowest rim of the basin, and continues on to lower levels. Lakes through which rivers pass are doomed. The river brings its deposits of earth particles into the inlet or "front door" of the lake, then drops them as it loses its velocity. Some lake basins gradually become almost filled with mud and silt, raising their elevation proportionately.

The presence of the river increases the speed of the water through the lake outlet, and also the erosion there. The river thus makes a larger and deeper outlet for the lake, causing the amount of water which the lake can hold to become less and less. Finally the channel grows so deep that it entirely drains the lake. Then the sediments remaining at the sides of the lake become hardened mud on the valley walls.

A young river eats its way to the highest and farthest point possible from its mouth; it becomes a kind of pirate. As the head of the river cuts across the divide, it may devour the channel of a neighboring river. In so doing, some or all of the captured stream is diverted into the channel of the pirate. The stolen waters make the pirate river greater in size, in drainage area, and in importance. Pirate rivers, however, are not common. It is interesting to discover one and explore the point where the river committed the act of piracy.

Some believe that the Umpqua River, in Oregon, once flowed into the Willamette River but was beheaded by the present Umpqua which now empties into the sea at Reedsport. The capture of the Umpqua is said to have occurred at Divide, Oregon, near Cottage Grove. Another example of river piracy is likely the Long Tom River, west of Eugene. This river could easily have been a tributary of the Siuslaw at one time and later been pirated by a tributary of the Willamette.

Sometime between youth and old age a river matures. Man and other animals reach this period at a fairly definite age, but since the life of a river occasionally runs into millions of years, its maturity cannot be pinned down with exactness. However, much like the waistline of a mature man, the river at this period also tends to spread out. Its straight course has developed a curving path so its valley is wider. The V-shape of youth is gone because the river, in fanning out, has cut away steep valley walls. Rapids and falls have been leveled and the lakes, which filled earlier basins, have been drained—or are shallow and marshy. When rapids, falls, and lakes disappear, youth is over.

The tributaries of the mature river lose their zest for dashing toward the main stream. They no longer leap down valley walls into the river, for the steep sides are gone. The land over which the tributaries flow is now rounded and subdued. Man in his youth plays and works strenuously but slows down with maturity. So it is with a river; the mature river washes its banks as before but it picks up the lighter, muddy sediments for its load — and drops them sooner.

Features displayed in maturity develop with old age. Curving channels become great sweeping meanders. Like the restless old man who whiles away the hours wandering about the community in which he lives, the old river in its crooked channel flows listlessly back and forth across the land. So extensive are these great curves that, in some instances, when floods occur, water pours across the low ground between the meanders to cut a new channel which in turn often isolates parts of river curves. If these isolated parts receive enough water to remain filled, they are called "oxbow lakes." Land surrounding an old river and its tributaries is almost level as, particle by particle, the land—which may even have been mountainous in the youthful days of the drainage pattern—has gradually been destroyed. These particles of sediment now rest in the depths of the sea. The land has helped destroy itself by cradling the runoff from its ancient peaks.

Signs of age in a river can be contradictory. In the State of Washington, for instance, the Yakima River, between Yakima and Ellensburg, meanders in a V-shaped channel—a sign here of old age as well as of youth. From the meander it appears that the river has reached maturity, or possibly old age. Probably, though, the land near it had been reduced to a plain, or nearly so; then the land rose, giving the river a steeper grade, more velocity, and more cutting power. Rejuvenated, the river resumed its work of deepening its channel. As the land rose, the river kept pace with its digging and a curved, V-shaped trench resulted.

Glaciers have a reputation for changing the life cycles of some rivers begun before the ice arrived. It is not uncommon to find a river flowing on top of sediments which fill the valley from side to side. These sediments, usually gravel and other glacial debris, were deposited in the valley by a glacier, or by water pouring from beneath the ice at the time of the glacial period. The river, which had in many instances carved its way deep into the rock of the area, probably ceased to exist during glacial times. Then, when the glacial disturbances were over, the river resumed its flow on top of the sediments which now choke the valley. A river needs eons of time to reach the rock bed on which it worked before the glacier came. After disturbance by both lava and glaciation, the Columbia River, in Washington, now flows on materials different from those of its ancient bed.

There are other signs of river age which are confusing. Sometimes different ages appear at different points along a river. A river first reaches maturity and old age at its mouth. However, because the materials along its course vary in hardness a river can age faster where these are more easily removed. Finally, land can be elevated in some places and not in others, to interrupt the regular cycle.

A River About to Retire

The Pacific Northwest has a youthful physiographic surface. Although at intervals during geologic time the Pacific Coast states were invaded by the sea, they also held a plain with hills that had been leveled by erosion. Nowadays the region supports mountains and volcanic peaks which originated in the latest of geologic eras. Typical of a youthful landscape with youthful rivers, the Pacific Northwest has many of the V-shaped valleys, especially in the mountains. In them rolls the rapidly falling water—busily downcutting these recently uplifted forms.

Milk River, rising in Glacier National Park, Montana, is an example of a river in the later stages of life. This 729-mile stream flows southeast into Canada, returns to Montana, and finally empties into the Missouri. In its youth, Milk River cut its course straight, with its water descending over boulder-strewn rapids and falls. Now its waters flow calmly, wandering back and forth, to find the easiest possible grade.

On a limited scale this river is still at work (Photo No. 55). In the foreground, a curved section is slowly cutting into its banks, at the same time leaving a piece of land behind. The side having the pointed land is shallow, while the side doing the cutting is deeper. No doubt Milk River once flowed between much higher hills than at present. The rock composing them has been slowly broken up, carried into the river by its numerous tributaries, then transported to faraway places, perhaps even to the ocean. Unimpressive now, the hills patiently wait for the meandering river to take what is left. Those living today will not see the plain in the making here, but a plain it will surely be, with tired Milk River barely able to find its way down whatever gradient happens to remain.

Photo No. 55   *U. S. Geological Survey*

Milk River, which rises in Glacier National Park, Montana, is an example of an old river, with its meanders and subdued topography. Notice the flat nature of the valley and the sluggish flow of the river.

The Snake River—A Study in Youth

Since the Pacific Northwest has a youthful topography, examples of young rivers are easy to find. The Snake River, though, stands out as a classic example. Perhaps nowhere else in America has a river bitten into a more rugged environment than the Snake (Photo No. 56). Rising from the water level of the Snake River is some of the most primitive, deeply-eroded, peak-strewn country in America. These are the unmistakable signs of youth.

The Snake River rises in Wyoming, in Jackson Hole, and shortly thereafter sweeps through the Teton Range, through which it has cut a gorge one half mile deep. For the next hundred miles it crosses the southern part of Idaho in a great southward

Photo No. 56   *Oregon State Highway Commission*

Grand Canyon of the Snake River, popularly known as Hell's Canyon. Deep in desolate wilderness, the Snake is a classic example of a young river. Its rugged canyon forms the boundary between Oregon and Idaho.

bend, running on to form the Idaho-Oregon boundary for many miles. Between Hagerman and Buhl, on U. S. Highway 30, water from Thousand Springs joins the westward-bound river. The volume of water from these springs, great enough to suggest a large underground river, is said to be sufficient to provide every person in the United States with one hundred gallons of water a day.

In Hell's Canyon of the Idaho-Oregon border, the youthful characteristics of the Snake are best exhibited. Here the river is at work in a V-shaped trench, deeper and narrower than the Grand Canyon. In fact the Snake River flows in the deepest river-eroded canyon on the North American continent. Some consider this to be the deepest ditch in the world. Water in this canyon does not flow—it races. The fall in the Snake through here is twelve and one-half feet per mile, whereas that of the Colorado is ten.

Rock at the bottom of Hell's Canyon is basic granite, the product of the up-welling of fluid rock in a bygone era. Capping this granite is the brown basalt of Columbia Plateau, a part of the great lava flood in northeastern Oregon and southeastern Washington. Disturbed by these two igneous masses is sedimentary rock in a variety of formations. The elevation of the mountains and the position of the basalt on them—higher than it occurs on the plateau to the north—suggests that the Hell's Canyon region is an uplifted area in which the Snake River has cut downward, keeping pace with the rising mountains.

Lost Rivers

Rivers are among our most scenic landscape features. Their work can be readily observed, except when they become lost underground. In central

Idaho, 3400 square miles of volcanic rock swallow streams and rivers, making the waters' whereabouts, in this desolate region, only conjecture. From the point where Henry's Fork joins the Snake, no streams enter this river downstream for a distance of two hundred miles.

Big Lost River heads in the Sawtooth Range and travels southeast for about ninety miles. The Pahsimeroi Mountains feed the Little Lost River, which also flows southeast for about the same distance. At one time both of these rivers emptied into the Snake.

With the coming of volcanic upheaval, both river and stream channels were wiped out. Today the water from these rivers spreads out over the lava plain and, in times of maximum runoff, it collects in shallow lakes. Then it disappears into the Lost River Sinks, about fifty miles north of American Falls. It is believed that the lower ends of Big and Little Lost Rivers are only about ten miles apart.

The destination of water from the Sinks is something of a mystery. There is a strong belief that it emerges 150 miles to the southwest at the Thousand Springs, whose waters enter the Snake River. If this be true, the Snake River was not robbed of water from Big and Little Lost Rivers by the volcanic disturbances in the north. Now the water is left to wander — out of sight for a time — before plunging into the Snake from these extraordinary springs.

Porous central Idaho holds vast amounts of subterranean water. It is said that, if you listen closely at some places in this area, you can hear underground rumblings suggestive of rushing water. This condition is typical of lava formations, famous for their underground cracks, faults, even tunnels and caves.

Oregon, too, has underground streams, one of which flows for half a mile through a part of Malheur Cave, before disappearing. This cave is on a side road between Follyfarm and Princeton. The passage holding the water is fifty feet wide and ten to twenty-five feet high. With its splendid water supply, the cave was once used by Paiute Indians as a stronghold against their enemies. Arrowheads, mortars and other artifacts are still found here.

Metolius River

Springs in Oregon feed numerous streams; they even supply considerable water for several rivers such as the Metolius. This is called the fastest river in the West; being only forty-six miles long, it is also one of the shortest. Rising in the springs which gush out of the base of Black Butte—a tree-covered volcanic mountain—it runs toward Mount Jefferson in an irregular course. It then flows east, south of the Warm Springs Indian Reservation, after which it dives through a gorge fifteen hundred feet deep, to enter the Deschutes River west of Madras.

The Yellowstone River

Countless pictures have been taken from Artist Point, a jagged rock abutment overlooking Yellowstone River and Falls in the Grand Canyon of the Yellowstone National Park (Photo No. 57). Here is another fine example of a young river with all the features of vigorous youth. The water in Yellowstone River can be observed in relation both to conditions existing when its cutting began and to the amount of work to be done before the end of the cycle.

The tremendous cut which the river has already gouged into hard volcanic rock is another convincing

Photo No. 57

Yellowstone Falls and River, Yellowstone National Park. Here is a fine example of a youthful river, with its steep valley sides, V-shaped canyon, falls, and fairly straight course.

example of river erosion. The depth of this magnificent gorge varies from eight hundred to eleven hundred feet, but the almost-level horizon suggests that this river is entrenching itself in a large plateau. The Yellowstone may have been at work here for several million years, yet its work has just begun.

Like the youthful Snake River, the Yellowstone flows in the V-shaped valley of the Grand Canyon. No sluggish-water features of maturity or old age appear anywhere in the canyon. White water abounds from rapids created by boulders and rock ledges in the river bed. There is no old stream meandering here. The Yellowstone is as yet too busy rushing down its fairly straight course to be concerned about swinging from side to side. And it has the waterfalls of youth—one of the loveliest of these showing across from Artist Point.

Ellensburg Formation

Running water has played a part in the location and extent of all the sedimentary deposits of the Pacific Northwest. Because today's rivers and streams are bolder attractions, it is easy to bypass the erosion records of ancient streams. These records are often close at hand, for Northwest rivers have exposed many of the early sediments, making it possible for geologists to piece together the story of their time. One such deposit, the Ellensburg Formation, which shows clearly in the Yakima Valley of Washington, has great historical significance.

At the close of the period in which sheets of lava were being spread upon the Columbia Plateau, there occurred a sinking of the land east of what is now the Cascade Range. In this depression was formed a large lake to which streams brought sediments from land on the west. But volcanic activity had not yet run its course. Even before the basalt flows declined, a great volcanic disturbance shook the Cascade region and vast amounts of andesite lava were poured over the western land. Explosions blew out large quantities of volcanic ash, pumice, and tuff. Meanwhile the Cascade region was being uplifted; rocks and the detritus, or debris, of volcanism were being crushed and folded. Steeper slopes in the west meant that streams now flowed faster and caused more erosion. Resulting masses of the andesite materials —gravel, mud, and volcanic ashes—were carried eastward into the lake awaiting the sediments. Occasionally these were associated with a sheet of basalt which erupted belatedly in the dying action of the once-powerful Columbia flood.

It is interesting to note that the sediments in the western part of the Yakima Valley are coarse, indicating that these were dropped in a margin of the lake close to the source of supply. Farther to the east and farther from the western shore of the lake, the sediments became fine silt, dust, and ash. Some of the finer deposits, farther from the Cascade margin, can be attributed to more volcanoes that had broken out in the Cascades. The sediments in the outer basin were either carried by water or blown a long distance by volcanoes. Some distance above Pasco, the banks of the Columbia are lined with thick layers of fine sediments that have become known as the White Bluffs. These are all a part of the volcanic activity in the Cascades and subsequent deposits from them.

Unmistakable in numerous road cuts in the Yakima Valley is the Ellensburg Formation—a white to light-yellow layer of unsorted gravel, sand, and volcanic particles. Although scenic Yakima River is close by, along U. S. Highway 97, the layer of prehistoric sediment on the other side of the road reminds us that in the time of its origin, this area would have been merely a scene of mud-clogged streams, falling volcanic ashes, and a lake discolored by the sediments being deposited in it.

One more important feature of rivers should be mentioned: they sometimes change channels. The Pacific Northwest has many of these old river channels, where a river flowed for a time long ago. Many can be seen along the Columbia. These changes occur when land rises or falls, when landslides temporarily block the river, or when flood water seeks new space. Exploring these old channels is interesting for the sightseer and sometimes profitable for the placer miner.

Chapter 9

SHORELINES AND SEASHORES

A seashore is a land set apart—no matter where it is found. It is a place where a continent ends, where surf rolls in on hard, packed sand, or batters a headland of resistant rock. It is a marginal battle line where land's eroding agents give way to a new and powerful foe. Oceans and ocean shores are incompatible. No great stability is ever observed where land and ocean meet. Always under attack by the forces of nature, the land finds one of its most vicious destroyers in the sea—which goes about its vandalism openly, hurtling itself against whatever blocks its path.

Especially do weaknesses in the land fall prey to the marauding sea. Pounding water quickly seeks out bedding planes and the joint system of shoreline rock. Sooner or later these weaknesses make sections of rock crumble, under the relentless slap of the sea—which, in major storms, is estimated to reach a force of three tons per square foot. Loosened pieces of rock fall to the beach where they are rolled and ground into still finer bits by the undertow. The sea conducts its onslaught with all resources at hand—sand, gravel, and even beach boulders, all are caught up and thrown against the land.

Out of all this battering by the sea have come some enchanting coast forms for Oregon and Washington. The quality of the scenery seems often to

Photo No. 58   *Oregon State Highway Commission*

Otter Crest, one of the loveliest sites along Oregon's 400-mile coastline, shows clearly how the ocean's destruction can often beautify the land. Here a rising mist reflects the late afternoon sun.

depend on the amount of coastline destruction—the more destruction, the better the scenery. This shows clearly at Otter Crest, on Oregon's U. S. Highway 101, but it is also evident along the entire Pacific coastline, where the chafing seas have sculptured fascinating land conformations (Photo No. 58.)

Sea Stacks

Taking advantage of joints in weaker rock—which separate areas of harder materials—the sea often quarries out the softer rock, leaving the more resistant portions as remnants surrounded by water.

Photo No. 59   *Oregon State Highway Commission*

Sea stacks—or land remnants—with Haystack Rock in the distance, seen from Ecola State Park on the northern Oregon coast. The mainland once extended to—probably beyond—the farthest remnant.

These are called "sea stacks" or "chimney islands." At Cannon Beach on the northern Oregon coast, are fine examples of such remnants, relinquished by the sea as it gnaws its way inland at Ecola State Park. In Photograph No. 59, Haystack Rock, largest of the group, looms in the background, rising 235 feet out of the surf. This famous monolith in the Cannon Beach area is said to be a remnant of igneous rock which flowed into the Astoria formation. Nearby are the Needles and imposing Tillamook Head. Sea stacks or chimney islands can also be seen just below the mouth of the Quillayute River on the Washington Coast; and at Bandon, Oregon, near the mouth of the Coquille River.

Work of the Waves

Quiet water does little or no erosive work; the waves take care of this. Though wind is chiefly responsible for waves, the character of the ocean bottom and the rotation of the earth help. Oddly enough, ocean water at any given point is essentially stationary. The wave reaches the distant shore, but not the water. Waves cause water particles to rotate in a circular path. Thus, when the wave passes, the disturbed water particles return just about to the point where they started. Waves in water resemble those in a field of grain. The stalks bend down in the wind but they straighten up to await the next movement of air.

On approaching land, the waves drag bottom, breaking the circular action of deeper water. The water then takes on a forward movement and foaming water rushes landward with the power of a battering ram. When large waves break ashore, their power is just as effective. Having spent its energy, the water, reclaimed by the sea through gravity, forms the undertow—or current beneath the surface—which can be dangerous to persons venturing too far.

Most of Oregon's exquisite beaches and scenic coastline features are skirted by a fine year-around highway, 397 miles long, with landscape beauty along every mile of it. Nowhere else in the Pacific Northwest has a coast highway of such nearness to the sea and such length been constructed. Nowhere else in North America has such a scenic route been built.

Types of Seacoasts

Seacoasts fall into four types. One shows the results of land movements, such as those responsible for the shifting mountains. A second shows the deposits that volcanoes have made along the shorelines and beyond. A third exhibits the work of glaciers which have gouged steep-walled inlets that now house deep, inland-reaching fiords. A fourth kind shows the results of faulting by the shore lands, with high, steep cliffs or escarpments rising along the coast. All of these varieties can be visited on Northwest shores.

Not all travelers along the beautiful Pacific coast have the time, or the inclination, to seek out the geologic details of the seashore features flashing into view. For some, attractive pictures of the trip will suffice. Others, who seek the why and how, will stop and investigate—will travel perhaps on foot to points where a phenomenon can be seen in relation to the surrounding country, where rock can be broken and studied, and where more detailed photographs are possible. For both kinds of travelers the coast route is recommended. One traveler will see outstanding coast forms that are probably different from any he has seen before; the other will also see these but, in addition, will have opened new vistas into the country's geologic past.

Coastal Changes

A map of the Northwest coast reveals that more indentations of the land occur north of the Strait of Juan de Fuca than south of it. Puget Sound, the largest embayment in the Pacific Northwest, is the beginning of a series of indentations which typify the coast northward along British Columbia, to and including southeastern Alaska. In general, this indicates that the coast south of the strait was elevated and the portion north was submerged. However, this generality does not apply to all local conditions. The mouth of the Columbia River is depressed or "drowned," allowing the tide to run upstream for 140 miles; similar conditions are in effect for twenty-five to thirty miles along the lower reaches of the Willapa, Chehalis, Coquille, and Umpqua rivers.

The character of the Oregon Coast changes markedly at the Coquille River. North of this point, outcroppings of shale and sandstone with igneous intrusions predominate. These are overlaid by Pleistocene sand and gravel. South of the Coquille the rock is harder and older and, for the most part, of Mesozoic Age. Here the shoreline has headlands of basaltic masses and bays in softer rock.

Capes Perpetua and Heceta

Headlands jutting seaward from a coastline cannot fail to attract attention. On the Oregon Coast these are usually igneous land spurs or flows which have resisted erosion. Capes Perpetua and Heceta are composed of basalt agglomerate; that is, they consist of cemented fragments of volcanic rock and tuff (finer volcanic detritus). Heceta Head has been cut by many basalt dikes, ranging in thickness up to four feet. Some believe that the basalt was erupted from vents a short distance to the northeast. Passage for U. S. Highway 101 was carved out of these headlands whose feet rest in the boiling surf far below. It is a sight well worth stopping for —to look down at the wild sea surging over the black rock remnants which nestle at the foot of the cliff.

Sea Lion Caves

A short distance south of Heceta Head, at the famous Sea Lion Caves, is an excellent place to observe volcanic agglomerate, as well as sea caves and an interesting kind of sea life. Those caves were formed by the action of waves pounding against the almost-perpendicular wall of volcanic basalt and agglomerate. The caves have two openings from the sea, which can be reached by stairway or elevator.

Photo No. 60   *Oregon State Highway Commission*

The only mainland sea lion rookery in the world is located in Oregon, north of Florence, on U. S. Highway 101. The work of ocean waves has created a haven for these great mammals—several of which can be seen here, resting on the rocks.

This refuge, the home of sea lions, is said to be the only mainland sea lion rookery in the world (Photo No. 60).

Pillow Lava

Cape Lookout, near Sandlake, Oregon, is perhaps the most scenic igneous headland on the Pacific coast, and it is one of the few headlands that cannot be reached by automobile. Yet, two miles of hiking in the sand will likely be forgotten when the features of this massive promontory are explored. Cape Lookout, about two miles in length, is the product of a long stream of lava which poured out of an earth-vent somewhere beyond the seacoast. The almost-vertical sea cliffs of this flow reach seven hundred feet in height. Although "pillow" lava appears at other points along the coast, this is one of the better places to observe it. Pillows of lava are formed when molten lava is suddenly cooled by water. Many of these rounded, hardened blobs are at the bottom of the Cape Lookout flow, proving that the lava coursed into the sea and was hardened by it.

Other lava outcroppings along the Oregon Coast are those of Tillamook Head and Otter Crest, which also have dikes of intruded basalt. These may be related to the basalt in the Astoria area. Near Agate Beach, Iron Mountain rises as an erosion remnant of a basalt intrusion—the basalt being a part of the igneous rock that arrived here in volcanic times. North of Newport, is Yaquina Head, which supports one of the many lighthouses along the coast. This great intrusion pushed aside softer materials to attain the position it now occupies. It is a good example of how softer materials have been worn away to leave the harder basalt, forming so many of the headlands along the Oregon Coast.

Depoe Bay

Depoe Bay, a resort and fishing village on the Oregon Coast, has a rare arrangement. Here in Miocene basalt the waves cut a bay almost rectangular in shape; then, finding a narrow zone of weakness in the middle of the shoreward rectangle, they proceeded to cut another bay ideally sheltered and now used by fishing boats. U. S. Highway 101 spans the channel between the outer and inner bays. On the hill behind lovely Depot Bay are the massive scars of the great Tillamook Burn.

Spouting Horns

Another product of the often-whimsical sea is the spouting horn. One of these is at Depoe Bay. Though it seems mysterious, it is really very simple on being examined at close range. When a tunnel, or miniature cave in rock, develops an overhead opening and waves surge against its entrance, pressure results which forces the water upward and out through the top of the vent. The spouting horn, casting its plume of spray into the air in Photograph No. 61, is located at Cooks Chasm, at Neptune State Park, north of Newport on the Oregon Coast. In this long, narrow and deep-wrought fissure, the sea often rolls in with spectacular fury.

Uplifted Seacoast

Much of the enchanting land of mountains and far-flung alpine ridge country of the Pacific Northwest is in position today because of tremendous forces which have arched them upward. Subsequent erosion has sharpened peaks and deepened valleys.

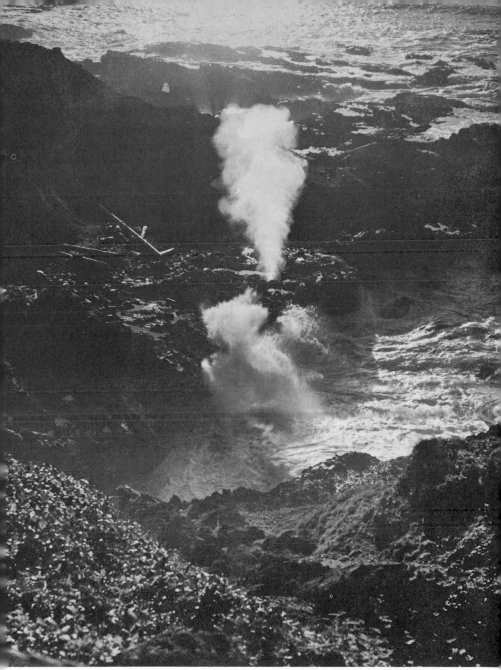

Photo No. 61   *Oregon State Highway Commission*

Here a spouting horn is spewing at Cooks Chasm at Neptune State Park north of Newport in Lincoln County, Oregon. This phenomenon is created by surf surging through water-carved tunnels which reach the surface of the rocks along the shoreline.

We know that elevation has occurred because of the upfolded formations exposed throughout the region. Most conclusive proof is that found in sedimentary rock resting at high elevations in the Cascade Mountains. Some sediments in the high country contain seashell fossils which seem decidedly out of place at this altitude. Fossils—six thousand feet above their place of origin, the sea—are dramatic proof of the amount of uplift which this region has experienced.

Brookings Terrace

Since portions of land along the Pacific Ocean have also risen, the coastline in these places is decidedly different from coastlines in other places. One of the best vantage spots from which to see an elevated beach is a flat area which begins north of Brookings, in southern coastal Oregon, and continues south for twelve miles. This area, about a mile in width, is an old ocean beach, now uplifted, on which surf once rolled landward as it does on today's beach—two hundred feet below. The town of Brookings is located on this ancient beach or terrace. A close observer will pick out tall, solitary rock spires, some 150 feet high, standing about on the flat Brookings shelf. These are sea stacks, igneous land remnants, which the sea failed to destroy before the land rose. The old shoreline is of course at the eastern edge of the narrow plain, where rocky cliffs rise abruptly from the ancient beach and its waveless sands.

Humbug Mountain

Can you picture a marine terrace on a mountain side? The Oregon Coast has two of these, north of the interesting Brookings terrace. The first, north of Brookings, is on Humbug Mountain, 1748 feet high and composed of cemented igneous pebbles (conglomerate). The mountain has a pointed appearance and is practically bare because trees have not been able to take root in the dense conglomerate. Though the road displaying many of the scenic features of the Oregon Coast passes along the eastern base of the mountain, do not look for the terrace here. The sea did its work from the west when, long ago, Humbug stood apart from the land as an island. There are, in fact, two terraces on this mountain, one at five hundred feet elevation and an upper one at a thousand feet. This reveals that, after the upper terrace was cut, the land rose, then rested long enough for the cutting of the lower terrace before it rose again. Bill's Peak, farther north, also has a marine terrace on its shoreward side.

Sections of the Oregon Coast Highway have been built along these terraces. One more deserves special mention—the terrace on Cape Blanco, the most westward point in Oregon. The top layers of this two-mile-wide terrace—about 170 feet above the sea—have yielded large amounts of clamshells. These shells differ only slightly from the shells of clams now living in the sand on the beach below. This clue reveals that the Cape Blanco terrace is a newcomer among the uplifted features of the coast.

Neahkahnie Mountain

Though faulted coastlines are not readily discernible along the Pacific Coast, there is one at Neahkahnie Mountain that is classically prominent. The top of Neahkahnie is seventeen hundred feet above the sea and nine hundred feet of this height is an almost perpendicular sea cliff—strongly suggesting that the sheer rock is faulted. This rock is likely responsible for the preservation of the fault plane above the waterline. That it is a very hard, igneous mass with some basalt is probably the reason it stands straight. Softer rock would surely have crumbled, defacing the faulted features. A considerable amount of this igneous rock came to rest in the Neahkahnie area. North of Neahkahnie, siltstone and sandstone beds have been enveloped by its intrusions.

British Columbia Fiords

The fiords on the west coast of British Columbia, in Canada, duplicate those in Norway. Here the mountains of the Coast Range dip steeply into the Pacific Ocean. Beginning near Vancouver, B. C., and continuing northward, long inlets of the sea reach into the land. Anyone privileged to explore these inlets by boat will find that they are in fact U-shaped glacial troughs whose valley walls, covered by dense coniferous forests, stretch upward more than four thousand feet. Severe glaciation has lowered the floors of some of these fiords to a thousand feet below water surface. Generally the fiords represent a potential recreation area of great beauty, with their deep water, green forests, clean air, and virgin wilderness.

Sand—A Sea Product

Sand is an ever-present product of all seashores. It is the residue of rock which has yielded to the battering of ocean waves and the constant grind of surf. Where resistant rock juts into the sea— such as the basalt found in many places on the Oregon Coast—little or no sand is present. However, on this coast, igneous headlands are separated by areas of softer rock in which indented sandy beaches offer splendid opportunity for beachcombing or swimming. Sand beaches range along the entire Pacific Coast—being extensive between Coos Bay and Heceta Head and also north of the Columbia.

The ocean works the sand into many interesting forms. Best known of these forms are the dunes caused when the sea casts up sand that, in time, is blown inland. A sand dune area, several miles wide, occurs between Seaside and the mouth of the Columbia River. Here the sand is laid in ridge-like forms. It is rather surprising to learn that the ocean did not make all of this vast accumulation of sand. A river, the Columbia, is the origin of much of it. Carried downriver from far-flung sources, the sand was first washed into the ocean where currents carried it south, then it was washed shoreward by waves toward the dune areas.

Winchester and Tillamook Bays

Sandspits are created when sediments, derived from headland erosion or from other sources, are deposited by littoral or coastal currents on the leeward side of a land projection. In time, a long finger of sand or gravel forms which may bar an embayment or create a sheltered harbor. Sandspits in Oregon are found at Coos Bay, Winchester Bay, and Tillamook Bay. Long Beach spit, in Washington, north of the Columbia River, is an ocean-built finger of land which in summer supports a booming tourist industry. Automobiles can be driven over twenty miles along the level, hard-packed sand, while ocean breakers roll in only a few feet away.

Eustatic Change

We must go back to the Pleistocene for an explanation of some features along the Pacific Coast.

In addition to the work of its glaciers, Pleistocene climatic conditions affected coastlines the world over. The formation of immense quantities of ice at that time consumed equally great amounts of water, so much that the oceans—suppliers of moisture for cyclonic storms—were lowered, possibly five hundred feet each time the ice advanced.

Four major periods of glaciation have visited North America. On the seacoasts during these periods, streams which normally entered the ocean at sea level were suspended above it. On the other hand, streams working on a steeper gradient lowered their mouth areas to coincide with the new level of the ocean. R. J. Russell, who has contributed much to American geology, states that during the last glacial age, called the Wisconsin, the Pacific Ocean stood 450 feet lower than its present level. He suggests that, were all the ice now on the earth to be melted, two hundred feet of water would be added to the elevation of the sea.

The lowering or rising of the sea by decreasing or increasing its volume is known as eustatic change in elevation. Since part of the Pacific Coast has experienced both uplift by land arch and eustatic change—determining the sequence of events which created the many marine terraces becomes very complex. The fact that glaciers remained active for a long time means that the ocean also stayed at its lower stage for perhaps thousands of years at a stretch. This development allowed time for the formation of new ocean beaches. Geologists are therefore often puzzled as to which of the natural historical events to assign to each of the coastline terraces.

The rising water of the oceans, when glacial melt water was released to them, brought an additional change to the often-altered Pacific Coast. Water entered recently-eroded river mouths, where for a time deep water existed. However, these mouths eventually filled with silt, resulting in rather shallow water in most coast harbors. Many of today's embayments have long barrier beaches and sandspits which protect harbors from the waves driven in by storms.

The seashore is ever changing. In 1939, a heavy storm severed the spit across Tillamook Bay in four places and its mountainous seas threatened the Bay Ocean resort on the spit. For a time, oyster beds in Tillamook Bay were even endangered.

Sand Lakes

Since sand is one of the most porous materials, it seems inconceivable that depressions in it can hold water in lakes. There are many such lakes, however, cupped in sand along the coast of the Pacific Northwest. Sand lakes are formed in stream channels by drifting dunes acting as dams, or by ocean waves throwing up a barrier at the mouth of a river. Siltcoos Lake, a body of water of considerable size in Lane County, Oregon, is a sand-blocked, shallow lake. Tenmile, Eel, and Tahkenitch Lakes have also been formed in sand-dammed depressions.

The seacoasts of Washington and Oregon are a fascinating place to study the changing form of the continent's edge. It is a world of its own—with the restless sea grinding its way into the land in some places and throwing off its stolen debris in others. It is a place where agates, fossils, and seashells can be collected and where the geologic ages have left their records in eroded, sedimentary, and faulted rock.

Chapter 10

DESERTS, DUNES, AND DUST

Though all land forms studied by geologists are more or less affected by climatic conditions, the desert and semiarid regions—because of their barren appearance, wind-eroded and wind-driven materials—seem to be more a product of climate than other landscape features. In general, the Pacific Northwest has two kinds of climate and each affects the land surface in various ways. The area west of the Cascades has a temperate marine climate in which mild winters and cool summers prevail. Rainfall ranges from 180 inches at some stations along the coast to about thirty-six inches at Seattle. The coast of Washington has the heaviest rainfall in the United States. East of the mountains, in the intermontane region, rainfall reaches twenty inches, with large portions of it having less than ten. Here, when the northers blow, winters are very cold. In contrast, summer temperatures of a hundred degrees are not uncommon. This is the dry continental which, like other climates, varies locally according to altitude, latitude and nearness to other climatic zones.

Erosion is directly related to precipitation. Stream erosion is constantly at work on the Pacific Northwest Coast because the abundant rainfall of the western slope provides a year-round flow of water. In contrast, river and stream erosion east of the Cascades—except for the major streams—is at times an intermittent process, for some streams contain water only during spring runoff. The division between the western and eastern parts of the Pacific Northwest is thus regulated by the amount of precipitation falling on a particular area.

The ocean produces sand when waves beat against rocky shores and break up the rock into tiny particles. During storms, large breakers carry these particles to ocean shorelines where they are left to dry on the beaches. Afterwards they are blown inland by ocean winds and it is here that the concept that sand deposits are associated with aridity breaks down. It is the pounding of waves and winds of high velocity which drives sand to an inland location. Sand and dunes found along the Pacific Coast are not formed by the conditions which make sand in the interior areas.

There are many sand-dune areas along this coast and most of these are easily accessible to the motorist, or the explorer on foot. The Pacific Ocean, pounding on hundreds of miles of Washington and Oregon coastline, throws up sand particles to form these dunes—which seem to lend themselves to the instinctive desire of people of all ages to shed their shoes and walk barefoot among them. And people the world over like to bask on the warm sand.

Oregon Beach Dunes

Ocean beach dunes are beautifully displayed at Coos Bay spit on the Oregon Coast. Here a sand beach extends southward from the Umpqua River for about twenty miles, ending in the spit, which juts across the bay for ten miles and is about three miles at its widest section. The wind-blown sand rolls in yellow symmetry, inviting the hiker to explore an expanse of clean sand and to visit a beach where fresh sand is constantly washed landward by the unceasing ocean currents. Such a vast collection of sand makes one wonder about its source. To be sure, much of it is being broken from the edge of the continent itself. The Umpqua River is doubtless a liberal contributor, bringing rock particles from its extensive basin to the ocean, where they are caught up by ocean currents and waves and finally come to rest in the dune-studded Coos Bay spit.

Another outstanding dune attraction in the Northwest is the Jessie M. Honeyman Memorial State Park on U. S. Highway 101, near Florence (Photo No. 62). This great dune area, shaped by the winds from the Pacific, is a sandy world set apart from the green forests and mountain chains of the region. By watching for road signs, the traveler along Oregon's Coast Highway can, with little effort, find a suitable place for entering the dune area on foot. He must first, though, walk through a strip of timber which in many places hides the dunes from motorists. When he has broken through the forest growth he beholds a different world.

Rounded dunes stretch seaward where the thundering ocean surf is loud. Here and there sand depressions hold small lakes. At the edge of the forest some barren skeletons of trees protrude from the drifted sand; they have not been able to withstand its smothering effects. The movement of sand at Honeyman State Park may have been partially arrested by the grass that has been planted to stabilize the dunes—which are headed toward forest growth and the busy highway. In this virgin, ocean-rimmed wilderness the neatly arranged, man-planted rows of grass present a striking impression.

Photo No. 62   *Oregon State Highway Commission*

A delicately-carved sand dune at Jessie Honeyman Memorial Park, near Florence, Oregon, along U. S. Coast Highway 101. The steep left side of this dune is the leeward side; the longer sloping side to the right is the windward.

Climate and Deserts

East of the Cascades, the deserts of the Pacific Northwest, with their sand and dust-made features, have been greatly influenced by the chemical and mechanical action of air, lack of moisture, freezing and thawing, and the fine materials supplied by running water. Air resting upon the earth's surface influences every particle which it contacts. Air lying above the earth extends upward for forty miles, pressing the land with a weight of thirty million tons per square mile. Whether it is motionless or moving—as wind—the air is always at work, transforming the land by movement of earth particles or chemistry.

Air is a combination of gases, chief of which are nitrogen and oxygen, with traces of ozone, argon, helium and others. Some of these substances are able to combine with minerals in the rocks. When this occurs, the rock disintegrates and crumbles, and it is then ready for transport by running water, ice, or wind. The active gases in air are oxygen, carbon dioxide and water vapor. Oxygen unites readily with iron to form iron oxide, or rust. When oxygen burns its mark into rock containing iron, it produces beautiful shades of red and yellow. Many rock formations have this common element. Carbon dioxide unites with calcium to form calcium carbonate. Water and carbon dioxide unite with orthoclase —feldspar, a mineral common in igneous rock—to yield kaolin, a very pure white clay. Thus the delicate teapot which graces a festive table may once have been part of a fire-formed block of granite, weathered into clay during countless ages, then dug from a pit, molded into shape, and fired once more to make gleaming china.

Because of its location in the area robbed of moisture by the Cascade Mountains, eastern Washington is an arid, inland basin, rimmed by the western Cascades on the west, the Okanogan Highlands on the north, and the Rocky Mountain Range east of Spokane. Where soil is available atop the basalt of Columbia Plateau, dry farming is practiced. The rock-strewn and eroded scablands might be classed as a rock desert. Little precipitation falls — barely enough to support grass for limited grazing.

The Potholes

In glacial times quantities of sand were washed southward by the meltwater from glaciers and the floods from the scablands of eastern Washington.

Since that time, the sand from this source has been scooped out by the wind, creating an area known as The Potholes. An aerial view of this region from the south shows a marked design in landscape pattern. Since the prevailing wind is southerly, the steep windward slopes of the dunes dip in that direction and large circular "blowouts" appear. The sand in The Potholes lies on the surface of the Columbia Plateau basalt, which in some depressions has been laid bare by the wind. Water that has collected in numerous depressions in the fall provides a resting place for thousands of ducks and geese in their southward flight.

Idaho Dunes

Northern Idaho has no desert areas, for this is a mountainous country of high peaks and coniferous forests. Much of central Idaho is a part of the plateau whose rock flowed into place from Oregon and Washington. Southern Idaho is a complex region, arid in nature, where rolling sage-covered terrain replaces the plateau and mountain country of the north. Here, in some places, very few rivers flow because they are swallowed by lava fields. It is logical that in this region lies one of Idaho's rare sand deserts.

This miniature Sahara is located northwest of St. Anthony. There, golden sand, ranging from ten to a hundred feet in depth, occupies a slope thirty miles long and less than two miles wide. Probably because of its narrow width, the sand in this picturesque little desert shifts in restless movements. It is said that this desert is never twice the same because of the action of the swirling wind.

Columbia River Dunes

Strangely, rivers also deliver material for sand dunes. Sand is deposited on the banks of rivers by waves, or dropped as sediments in times of high water. Sunlight which dries the particles and wind which lifts them to higher ground sets in motion the process of dune formation. In the Northwest, the Columbia River has created several dune areas on its route to the sea. At intervals along the river in north central Washington — and especially at Vantage, where the Columbia cuts through a portion of the Columbia Plateau basalt—dunes are now taking shape. Working up from the river, they have created a problem for the Washington State Highway Department. Winds blow off the river and up the steep banks. As they do so, the sand dunes are propelled upward over U. S. Highway 10 which descends the east wall of the river channel, on that side of the river—then crosses the Columbia at Vantage. Since clearing the highway is sometimes necessary, sand fences have been strung along to slow the movement of the sand dunes. Farther on down the river, where no highway is involved, sand—following the same upward climb—has risen to the rim of the plateau, which here is at least two hundred feet above the river.

Formation of Dunes

Dunes usually pose the question—how are they formed? Perhaps the best way to explain how most dunes originate is by describing how anyone can start a dune, that is, if he happens to live near a place where wind carries sand particles over the land. Dunes form when some obstruction brings the particles to rest on the ground. If a wooden crate, a board, or a fair-sized rock is placed on the ground, sand soon lodges around it. At first, sand will not collect close to the side of the object, which itself causes air immediately around it to swirl with increased velocity. Sand settles on lee sides of the obstruction where the wind is quieter. As the obstruction becomes covered, the sand itself, in time, also becomes an obstruction, capable of stopping sand particles flying along the ground. A few particles of sand deposited each time the wind blows gradually builds the dune. And, always, under each dune there is some obstruction—a rock, a clump of brush or grass, a fallen tree, or uneven ground—which caused the wind to drop a part of its load.

Every dune has a long, gradually-sloping side and a short, steep side. The gradual side is the windward grade up which the wind blows, rolling the sand particles from the lowest point at the bottom of the slope to the crest or divide of the sand ridge. When the particles reach the top they roll down the steep or sheltered side, where they come to rest. Desert travelers must seek the gradual windward slopes. The leeward sides are often impassable.

Traveling dunes are often fierce destroyers of landscape features and man's installations. Fences, farm buildings, and roads have been covered or otherwise made unfit for use by the steady advance of sand. It often smothers and kills forest vegetation adjacent to its domain. Desert sand south of Boardman, in eastern Oregon, has often crept right into ranch homes. Land has been obliterated and some buildings have been all but buried. On occasion, their owners have boarded up the buildings and left them to the sweep of the sand-laden winds.

Oregon Ghost Forests

Hunters are usually keen observers of the land-scape because, in hunting, landmarks must be kept in mind to establish direction, and, too, all things in nature interest most hunters. Oregon hunters who visit the plateau east of the Deschutes area have come in with descriptions of "ghost forests" seen in the country east of the Paulinas. Several groups of juniper trees have been reported from this little-visited region but the one which has attracted most attention is the one of several hundred acres south-east of Pine Mountain. Another well-known one is twelve miles south of Sand Springs. This is a land of volcanic pumice, a desolate land of fault scarps and volcanic buttes. It is a dry, desert wilderness, unin-habited except for scattered cattlemen.

Hunters, alone in this quiet, desolate region, are impressed by the gray, leafless junipers, weathered and sunbeaten, standing like ghosts in a cemetery of sand. These gnarled, dead junipers on the plateau were desert acclimated, slow growing, drought re-sistant—and supposed to live for centuries. What, then, killed them?

When hunters and foresters talk about the mystery of the ghost junipers, several opinions are voiced. Worms have been blamed because worm-eaten grooves are noticeable in the wood. Like all forms of life, trees mature and die, but this cycle would not account for the trees dying en masse. Fire has been suspected but no burns have been found. Sand, however, is a known killer. There are sand dunes northeast of the dead trees and it may be that these sharp-edged particles scoured the bark from the trees as they blew across the area. No one knows how deep the sand might have been among the junipers but, if the trees were once covered, they could have died from lack of air.

Unlikely Pine Forest

There is another interesting forest in the same general area, northeast of Fossil Lake, in Lake County. This is a live pine forest, unusual because it is located on the edge of a desert, far from other pines. These trees, though, may be in danger soon since dune sand is moving toward them from old lake beds in the northern part of the Great Basin. Foresters often ask why the pines are growing in such an unlikely place and how they have survived in this rigorous environment. Water from unknown sources must be providing life for them and—as for their location far from typical pine areas—it must be recalled that the wind is a capable transporter of seeds. Tumbleweeds have been blown across entire states, scattering their undesirable seeds for a new generation of these weeds. Plant seeds, the world over, are scattered by the wind. A few seeds successfully transported by wind to a source of water on the edge of a desert might well have resulted in an exotic forest of pines.

The Drying Northwest

Is the Pacific Northwest becoming drier? It would be rash to assume a drying period for the region as a whole, yet there are portions of it where much less water appears than in former times. Many of its lakes have partially or wholly disappeared, providing fertile areas for agriculture. And these changes have occurred within the memory of a single generation. Several conditions contribute to these changes. Man has lowered many lakes by drawing off water for irrigation. Volcanic rock, with its often-porous consistency and subterranean conduits, is a notorious robber of water. Oregon has many such formations, perhaps many yet unknown, into which water gradually seeps. One must remember that the dry air of eastern Oregon and Washington evaporates more water than the moister air along the coast. When the rate of evaporation exceeds the amount of water which is supplied by precipitation, lakes become marshes or exposed farm land into which man can sink his plow.

Central Oregon Deserts

The most extensive desert region in the Northwest is in south central Oregon. Geographically it is a westward extension of the Great Basin of Utah and Nevada. In this basin, water evaporates, sinks into the ground, or in some way disappears—none of it reaches the ocean. It is a land of dried-up lake beds, salt lakes, and washes of alluvial material interspersed with block-faulted mountains. The mountains are separated by basins in which salt deposits and sand dunes are the dominant land features.

Forested mountains and cool streams entice more visitors than deserts but deserts have a peculiar fascination. There is beauty in the flat, quiet, wasteland with its volcanic buttes jutting up through the pumice floors of the basin. Trees are absent here; not even the hardy juniper can take root and grow. Light snowfall in winter and occasional showers give the region no more than eight inches of precipitation a year. Because this soaks into the porous earth before streams can form, there are no watering places. It is a vast, empty land where wind blows across green sage, and the distant horizon outlines old mountains and volcanic buttes.

Every landscape has some features which give a clue to at least a part of its geologic history. Such a clue is not hard to find in the Great Sandy Desert, where there are convincing signs of once-abundant water. There are old lake beds as well as old river channels—even water-eroded canyons and valleys. One old river bed is outstanding. It heads northwest from Glass Buttes and after seventy-five miles enters the Deschutes Canyon. This narrow, steep-walled channel, now dry, was cut in basalt four hundred feet deep. This means that, ages ago, water flowed in the old river over a long period of time. What dried this large intermontane basin, stopping the flow of the deeply-entrenched river in the black basalt? This is one of the desert's mysteries which challenges scientists and adds zest to scenic geology.

On a drive west from Burns, Oregon, on U. S. Highway 20, the desert discloses many prominent landmarks. Old volcanoes, Placidia Butte, Glass Buttes, and Hampton Butte stand as sentinels of another age—and many young volcanic cones dot the landscape. These are so recent that the processes of erosion have scarcely marked their sides. The traveler can identify the younger cones by remembering that they are composed of basalt, whereas the older ones were of erupted andesite. The Great Sandy Desert area was not always as flat as it is today. This was a region of broken mountains and volcanic peaks until seventy-five feet of pumice and dust from the many volcanic outlets fell in the depressions between the peaks.

Since pumice and dust are the chief ingredients of Oregon's Sandy Desert, the word "sandy" is used rather loosely. A real sand desert, however, exists in

Lake County, east of Fossil Lake. In this enlongated, east-west desert the dunes cover about twenty-five square miles. Since this is the kind of dune area that moves, its boundaries vary, shifting into interesting crescent forms—however, its quantity of sand remains about the same.

The vastness of Oregon's southeastern desert is again evident on roads south out of Burns, which lead to the Steens Mountain and the Alvord Desert. This, too, is a sparsely-settled desert wilderness of sagebrush, unproductive earth and rattlesnakes. Steens Mountain receives considerable snowfall with the melt water rushing down the east face of the escarpment to the flat below. Nevertheless, the desert profits little from the runoff because the water is absorbed by the porous covering of the Alvord Desert, a flat playa, or desert basin, twelve miles wide and twenty miles long, which glistens with white potash. This lake bed is so smooth and hard packed that motorists who have driven on it find it difficult to resist testing the maximum speed of their cars.

Lake beds in desert regions where water has collected and evaporated often contain mineral salts. Southeastern Oregon is no exception. It is dotted with dry lakes in which these salts have gradually built up. A few of these have been of economic value. Borax Lakes at the edge of the Alvord Desert once produced large amounts of borax.

Exfoliation

There is yet another way in which the land is destroyed. It is of such importance that all persons interested in land forms should learn to recognize it. This is by the process of heating and cooling. Most substances expand when heated and contract when cooled. Rock follows the general rule, but this action sometimes fractures the rock. The camper who builds a fire, or surrounds the fire with stones to support a grate, will occasionally hear a popping sound as one of the stones breaks. The heat has caused this.

Through condensation, air supplies moisture to the earth. The most important forms of condensation are rain and snow, but large amounts of moisture collect on land surfaces in the form of dew. Ever seeking lower levels, water seeps into the cracks of all bodies of rock. But when heated and cooled, water reacts differently from most substances. As it freezes it expands, and when warmed it contracts slightly. Water expands about one-tenth of its volume when in a solid state. By expanding when it freezes, it acts as a wedge to break up rock that it enters. Slowly the rocks nearest the surface are fractured by the prying action of freezing water. The beautiful, sharp spurs and notched skyline of the Northwest's high mountain country have largely been created by the freezing and thawing of moisture at these altitudes.

Exfoliation, that is, the flaking of rock particles from a rock surface, is not accomplished by freezing and thawing alone. Much rock deterioration results from chemical weathering which causes rock minerals to swell and leave the rock mass. In some places rock particles appear under lichens. When the processes of exfoliation have finally finished their job in an area, no rock remains above ground level—all is now soil. Exfoliation is at work throughout the Pacific Northwest and throughout the world—wherever rock is exposed. Explorers of the outdoors are especially aware of its constant crumbling of the earth, which is nature's way of preparing its rocky forms for easy transportation.

Silent City of Rocks

On every part of our regional landscape, the usual weathered features have been, or are in the process of being, formed. Sometimes nature uses ordinary methods to fashion most unusual features. Such a feature occurs at the Silent City of Rocks, twenty-four miles from Burley, Idaho, via Oakley. In this area, a large granitic dome, twenty-five square miles in extent, has been weathered into a collection of fantastic figures.

Weirdness prevails in this area. Granite has been broken, rounded, indented and pointed, to assume a variety of shapes which, with a little imagination, resemble animate and structural objects. Some clearly reflect the names attached to them—Old Hen and Chicks, Giant Toadstool, Old Woman, The Dragon's Head, and Elephant Rock. There are rocky "buildings" of a city skyline with turrets and spires, 250 feet high. "Mosques" even rise from this city's floor —and all suggest the crowded pattern of metropolitan construction. In this silent city with its granite monuments, one can climb two hundred feet to the top of Bathtub Rock, whose concave top catches rain water in which phantom giants might bathe.

The area was known and visited long before the Northwest was extensively populated and long before interstate highways made travel easy. Probably because of its identifiable character it became the junction of the Sublette Cutoff and the California Road. In time, its granite walls became the register for thousands of names, dates and messages —records of those who had passed that way, or messages left for those who had not yet arrived. Here is said to be the largest collection of this kind of information found anywhere.

Palouse Country—A Wind-Deposited Landscape

Dust is an ever-present part of the envelope of air which encircles the earth. There will be fine particles floating in this medium as long as the earth's crust crumbles and is stirred by the wind, as long as volcanoes erupt, and as long as the surface of the earth is disturbed by man. Dust is such fine earth that it can remain in the air for weeks. It falls on ships in mid-ocean and on mountain snow fields. It is even possible that every place on the globe contains dust transported there from every other place.

Wind-blown deposits are responsible for the topographic features of many areas of the earth. Most interesting of these are the ones composed of loess, a buff-colored silt with particles ranging in size between sand and clay. Loess deposits occur in widely-separated places, being found in the Palouse region in Washington State (Photo No. 63), the Mississippi Basin, parts of China and Europe, and, surprisingly—on the campus of the University of Alaska. In Washington, this fertile soil produces much of the wheat grown in that state. Here the loess lies atop a portion of the Columbia Basalt Plateau. It has no relation to the dark, igneous rock underneath; that is, the loess has not been weathered from it. Palouse soil covers the eastern part of Adams and much of Walla Walla, Columbia, Garfield and Asotin counties. It skirts the Blue Mountains, reaching into Idaho, where it is the dominant soil of Latah County.

Most geologists who have studied the tremendous loess deposits in Washington and Idaho, agree

Photo No.63   *Washington State Advertising Commission*

Rolling Palouse Country in eastern Washington, a prosperous wheat-producing region. The loess soil composing these hills is thought to have been deposited by prehistoric winds.

that the particles, lying in the rounded hills of the Palouse, were wind deposited. However, the arrangement of the loess layers and their origin is a puzzle that has been examined in both lay and professional papers. In general, the top layer of soil in this region is a fertile silt loam. Beneath this layer there are about thirty-six inches of lighter brown soil and under it lie fifty to seventy-five feet of light yellow loess.

The puzzle is this—what sort of wind system laid this vast amount of dust-like soil on the basalt of the last lava flow, and whence was it transported? The loess is hard, much like fine sediments found in lake bottoms. It may well be that the fine material was left in depressions into which the outwash from glaciers poured exceedingly fine sediments. Later, when the arid climate was established east of the

Cascade Mountains, this fine earth might have dried, crumbled, and been blown into place from its lacustrine, or lake, bed.

Anyone who drives through the Palouse hills—over which crawls the power-driven equipment of the modern-day wheat farmer—must wonder why so much of this dusty soil is concentrated in this particular area. Here is one interesting theory which has been advanced:

The region receives from eighteen to twenty-two inches of rainfall annually, making it considerably wetter than some of the neighboring areas. Dust, blown from a dry region, is caught by an area having more moisture. Since dust storms still blow in the Palouse, some soil is being deposited in this manner. The cultivation of loess areas south and west of the moister parts of the Palouse country furnishes dust for the prevailing south west winds. Statistics reveal that the dust-fall in the Palouse hills amounts to 7500 pounds per acre each year. In a century this would build up four inches of soil. At this rate, nearly twenty-three thousand years would be required for the accumulation of seventy-five feet of loess. Has the present rate of soil deposit been the rule for this length of time? This will remain forever a mystery. No one has yet discovered the origin of loess deposits nor has anyone learned whether the prehistoric winds which deposited the millions of tons of loess were strong or light. However, it is easy to imagine the sun as being hidden in the blackness by the swirling, yellow dust which drifted into great mounds to cover the existing landscape for hundreds of square miles.

Washington Dust Storms

Many people in eastern Washington remember the dust storms of the 1920s and early 1930s. Loosened by plowing in the Palouse country, dust rose in dense, ominous clouds, blotting out light as it traveled north. Residents of Spokane called these storms "lalapalousers." A yellow pall of dust five hundred to a thousand feet high, rolling up in the south, heralded the approach of wind-blown dust. Soon it had arrived, seeping into homes and stores. At times the wind had been spent when dust reached a particular community. Yakima can remember when dust settled for a week in dead air, choking residents and falling, unwelcome, on everything. Windstorms which wheat farmers called "big blows" actually scoured away their valuable soil. Some blows carried away the finer, more fertile particles from wide strips between Pasco and Walla Walla, leaving coarser particles behind. After one of these storms, wheat would not grow successfully in the strips for several years. Soil drifts reached as high as fence posts in parts of the area.

Farmers—largely responsible for loosening the material for the lalapalousers and big blows—have hit upon a technique which has greatly reduced wind erosion. Wheat farmers who allow part of their acreage to remain unproductive on alternate years, to conserve moisture, now practice "trashy fallow." This consists of loosening the soil beneath the surface by means of a steel bar or series of spade-like cultivators which leave wheat stubble in a standing position. By making a mulch in this manner, stubble acts as a binder to reduce dust-forming conditions. Much soil is thereby conserved.

A canyon-desert extends for fifty miles from Moxee, Washington, to the Columbia River. In this extensive depression, sand dunes and dust mounds have accumulated during a long succession of windstorms. Persons who have experienced these storms remember them well—the pitted windshields, the wind-blown soil collected along fence lines, and the swirling sand up to six inches deep on the road to the river. A wind whipping down the canyon and yellow dust billowing into the sky means that low visibility is close at hand. Looking west from the White Bluffs region, close by Moxee Canyon, one may observe the effects of wind erosion through the ages. Topsoil has been removed from the river bluffs, exposing pure, white sand. As the rays of the setting sun glance off the White Bluffs along the Columbia, myriads of colors blend with the dying light to create an unforgettable picture.

Oregon Dust Storms

Oregon also has its dust storms. In the eastern part of the state there are the "dusters," some coming as squalls in advance of electric storms during the dry summer months. Others form in high southwest windstorms blowing in from the Pacific Ocean. Dust varies according to the wetness of the season. In the dry summers of 1959 and 1960, more dust appeared than in average years. Dust storms here are not like those which billow at high altitudes in the Midwest—here they hug the ground.

The northern Great Basin, in south central Oregon, is a wind-swept region where fine particles of Pleistocene lake beds are whipped into the air. Swirling dust is a common sight on Summer Lake. In eastern Lake County, extensive dunes have built up from the sand and dust of old lake beds and also from soil out of abandoned high desert fields which pioneers attempted to reclaim some fifty years ago.

The Columbia River Gorge directs ocean winds into the interior. Blasted through this deep corridor, air picks up sand and dust which floats in yellow billows above the river area. Old-timers still talk about a terrible dust storm in the gorge, many years ago, which lifted large amounts of fine soil into the sky. The dust mixed with clouds of a spring snow storm to result in a mantle of soil-stained snow on the land upriver.

The blanket of soil covering the earth's rocky core must be protected by vegetation, or be closely cemented, to resist transportation to some new locality. The elements seek out every weakness. As soon as a frailty is found, some kind of destruction begins.

Man was responsible for the disturbance taking place in the coarse layer of sand shown in Photograph No. 64. In choosing a route for a country road to the hills behind Okanogan Valley, near Tonasket, Washington, he built a road up a tributary canyon. During construction a bulldozer exposed the sand and gravel along the canyon side. This deposit, more loosely laid than the rest, was finally cut so that the wind, as it worked up and down the canyon, could begin its etching. Some layers were eroded faster than others, those resisting the wind being composed of coarser particles than the loosened layers. These resisting layers—actually shelves several inches in width—were found to crumble readily in the hand, but, when pieces were examined, their particles appeared lightly cemented by a grayish substance.

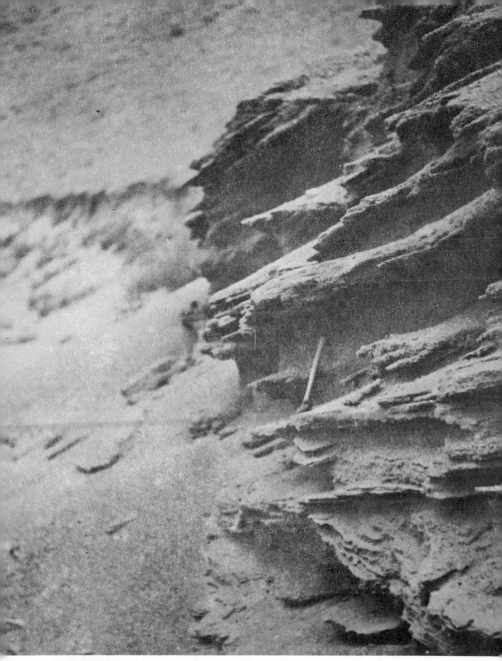

Photo No. 64

Wind-eroded road bank in Okanogan County, Washington. These layers appear to
represent seasonal deposits of river-carried sand. The protruding layers, which have
better withstood erosion, contain a cementing substance offering more resistance to
the wind.

This was why a series of shelves was eroding more slowly than the rest of the canyon wall.

These coarse and fine layers possibly represent seasonal deposits. From the way in which sand and gravel are laid down by water, we know that rapidly-flowing water carries coarser particles but drops them first when velocity slackens. This was probably the case with these layers, but it is strange that the cementing material is present only in the coarse sand. The fact that some of the layers of fine sand are thicker than the cemented layers could be explained if the area experienced longer periods of slow-flowing water than of rapid runoff.

This interesting formation juts out prominently from the steep hillside, an ideal location for the sweep of the wind. There will come a time, however, when the wind will have to work harder to continue its erosion here. This time will come when the height of the layers is in line with the rest of the hillside. The sloping valley wall—on which the layered deposits rest—will protect them from the cutting power of the wind. It may be that the hillside will slump down over these layers and completely hide them, but, should this happen, the sandy slope by the side of the road will have lost its unusual appeal.

Chapter 11

FAULTS—TRIGGERS FOR DISASTER

Faults, like other earth features, can decide the landscape pattern in a particular area and, under certain conditions, these cracks or weaknesses in the earth's crust can cause disaster. In the Pacific Northwest there are a number of unique land forms which have resulted from faulting. Throughout the Cascades, faults are quite common; also in western Montana, northern Idaho, and south central Oregon —where large block mountains have been topographically arranged by this process. Streams are famous for seeking out weaknesses in which to establish their channels. Because of their crumbled rock and frequent ditch-like depressions, faults make good stream beds. Oneonta Falls, which plunges down the basalt bordering the Columbia River Highway, may be at work in a fault zone. If not a fault zone, Oneonta Falls has found a fracture zone, quite common in basalt, in which to sink its bed (Photo No. 65).

Anyone who examines rock formations will notice that these are interlaced with cracks, some of which reveal prominent bedding planes. This is especially true in the case of rocks of sedimentary origin. Other kinds of rocks have cracks which run perpendicularly or at an angle. Very few rock deposits occur which are not broken and jointed in

Photo No. 65　　　　　　　　　　　　*Oregon State Highway Commission*

Oneonta Falls plunges down the basalt which borders the Columbia River Highway.
Judging from the sheer right wall of the ravine and the softer rock over which the
water flows, this stream is at work in a fracture or fault zone.

some part of their structure. Faults can be considered major cracks in the earth, but they are more than just cracks. They are the zones where large rock masses rub or slide against each other. Once these rock zones are found, their direction, amount of slippage, and the character of the fault plane, provide much interesting study.

For rock masses to move up or down, the faults which separate them must be vertical or nearly vertical. Earth slippage along a fault leaves many signs of earth movement—in fact, movement has to occur to make a fault what it is. All important faults, if any of the surfaces are visible, show signs of grinding and polishing. Such friction can produce polished surfaces, parallel scratches, or even grooving much like a corrugated roof. Fault scratches should not be confused with those made by rock carried in glacial ice. Glacially-caused scratches run in crisscross directions. At times, fault zones contain crushed and powdered rock because, when earth sections move, the sandwiched particles roll and grind into still finer particles.

There is another sign that indicates portions of rock masses have moved along faults. This is easily spotted in the faulting of bedded rock. When this slips upward or downward, the bedding pattern is displaced; that is, the various layers do not continue as even beds—especially if they are composed of different materials or colors. They then appear step-like. Many of these arrangements occur in the Cascades, where sills of igneous rock have been injected into rock of a different color. The displaced position of the sills gives the direction and amount of rock movement.

To the casual eye, a range of mountains and a rolling countryside appear wonderfully stable. Yet mountains do move upward and downward, but only in infinite slowness do their sprawling forms arch and bend. Besides, erosion by rivers and glaciers reduces the size of mountains as rock particles shift or are blown away. Sooner or later the mountain has to adjust to this shifting and sorting; great blocks of earth and rock must break to settle into better balanced positions. More faults develop as the need for them continues. Considerable movement can be measured along some faults. Along others their first displacement seems to have been their last.

Many portions of the Northwest surface are fault formed. The straight courses of some valleys—often so direct that they seem to have been surveyed by man—suggest that long sections of land dropped downward to shape these abrupt valley walls. When faults occur on ocean coastlines, sea cliffs are formed. The bold cliffs of Neahkahnie Mountain are an excellent example of a faulted coast. Some valleys here hang in mid-air—cut off by faulting.

Faulting in Montana

Part of the Clark Fork Valley in western Montana, through which flows the beautiful Clark Fork River, is an area of much faulting. Steep, almost vertical cliffs of brown, bedded rock line the western part of the valley for several miles. At St. Regis, the Clark Fork turns sharply east to cut through a section of the Bitterroot Range, then swings northwest a short distance east of Paradise. The canyon of the Clark Fork through the Bitterroot Range is one of the most scenic drives in western Montana. Abrupt cliffs and talus slopes soar up from the river as it twists and eddies between rocky abutments. Near Paradise, the Clark Fork is joined by the Flathead River which heads near the Continental Divide, south of Glacier National Park. The lower part of the river then flows between the walls of a long valley graben with its high cliffs and their great blocks of bedded rock.

More block cliffs occur along the Clark Fork near Eddy and Thompson Falls, becoming fewer as the river reaches its end at Lake Coeur d'Alene. Though the Clark Fork Valley now contains immense amounts of Lake Missoula sediments, its walls rise abruptly from the flat floor, suggesting that a large wedge of rock settled below the level of the bordering mountains, to form a drainage avenue from the Rocky Mountains by the Clark Fork River.

Another highly faulted area is Glacier National Park. In the arching process which built the mountains here, great blocks of rock, of sedimentary origin, were twisted and set apart. Between these, streams and glaciers have cut deep valleys. However, the basin and range region in Oregon have the distinction of possessing the most classic block-faulted mountains in the Pacific Northwest. This area is a part of the Great Basin which occupies Arizona, Nevada, New Mexico, Utah, southern Idaho, and a section of California. Throughout that segment of the basin located in Oregon, fault-block mountains, or tilted fault-blocks which trend north, rise from the graben depressions which separate them.

Oregon's Faulted Land

A giant large enough to stride across the State of Oregon could, in the southern portion, step on block-formed mountains or in flat basins between them. Beginning on the west side and going east, these areas would include the Klamath Lake Basin, Abert Lake Basin, Abert Rim, Warner Mountain,

Warner Valley, Hart Mountain, Catlow Valley, the
Steens and Pueblo mountains, the Alvord Desert and
the Owyhee Valley. Most of the mountains are more
than four thousand feet in elevation. Steens Mountain, with a 9670-foot elevation, is the highest. All of
them are bounded by faults. A fault map of Oregon
shows a series of broken, parallel lines, trending
roughly in a northwest, southeast direction.

The grabens, or basins, separating the mountain
blocks—in some instances surrounding them — are
arid pumice and dust flats which support only sagebrush and desert grass. Rainfall averages between
seven and ten inches per year. The water from intermittent mountain streams is absorbed by the blotter-
like pumice, sand, and dust of the basin bottom.
Where water remains above the surface in shallow
lakes, it is saline. Only in the Owyhee and Klamath
rivers can water reach the sea from this area.

Some of the features formed by faults in Oregon
are outstanding. One of these is found in the southeast corner of the state, a desolate yet scenic part of
Oregon. In a prehistoric age, the fault along U. S.
Highway 395, north of Lakeview and Valley Falls,
experienced a severe earthquake, or perhaps a succession of such disturbances. The fault where this
movement occurred is known as Abert Rim, considered to be one of the largest earthquake faults in
the world. The rim of its sheer escarpment (Photo
No. 66) rises 2500 feet above the valley floor. This immense displacement means that the valley either
sank below the level of the rim, or the rim was
pushed up beyond the level of the valley, or both.

Lakeview, south of famous Abert Rim, is located
on a major fault. Its position, almost directly in
line with the great prehistoric displacement in the
north, suggests that it may be related to the Abert

Photo No. 66   *Oregon State Highway Commission*

Abert Rim, a great prehistoric fault escarpment, lies along U. S. Highway 359, north of Lakeview and Valley Falls, Oregon. The fault has a displacement of 2500 feet and is thought to be earthquake caused.

fault. The hot water flowing from the ground at Lakeview is attributed to this fracture. Proof that the fracture exists lies in the occasional mild earthquakes. Northeast of Lakeview, Warner Lakes occupy a long depression, one of many in this region. Long ago, the surface of these lakes stood more than two hundred feet higher than its elevation today. Should the arid conditions here continue, Warner Lakes would soon disappear. Their trench or depression is bounded on the east by an enormous wall of basalt several thousand feet high and several miles long. The topmost point on this monumental block of basalt is Hart Mountain, with an elevation of 8030 feet.

The even alignment of the High Cascades, in a north-south trend, is probably the result of a fault something like this: The eastern side of the rock, along the fault, dropped downward. Then peaks, such as the Three Sisters, were built by volcanic eruptions, to remain in line along the fault. Geologists point out that springs, such as those at Belknap, Kitson and McCredie, are likewise formed in a line, suggesting that these, too, are located along a fault.

A fault, or perhaps a major earth fracture, may have determined the channel for the most scenic river of southeastern Oregon. This river is the Owyhee, which heads in southwestern Idaho, then enters the southeastern corner of Oregon and flows generally northward to join the Snake River near Adrian. In eastern Malheur County, the river has cut one of the deepest canyons in the west, in a rhyolite flow. This canyon is remarkable because the Owyhee River, unlike the rampaging Snake, is much smaller, so—much quieter. Only during the spring runoff does the river carry a sizable amount of water. Like its neighbor, the Snake, the box canyon of the Owyhee is very difficult to enter; travel throughout its length is not possible (Photo No. 67).

Most of this steep-walled gorge is now filled with water behind the Owyhee Dam, built across the lower end of the canyon. The granite walls can today be viewed by boat instead of by means of uncertain travel from bar to bar as in the days when the Owyhee ran unfettered through its deep-cut route to the Snake.

Earth Scars in Idaho

Near Cleft, Idaho, the earth has been scarred by two tremendous geologic events which easily excite the imagination. The first of these is found in two large volcanic pits that resemble bare-sided amphitheaters. At some time in the misty geologic past, both of these volcanoes exploded in a terrific outburst of fire and dust. In the cataclysmic change

Photo No.67   *Oregon State Highway Commission*

Owyhee River cuts through massive granite in Malheur County in eastern Oregon. A fracture zone is said to have provided the original line of entry for the small yet powerfully-erosive Owyhee.

which shook the area, a cubic mile of rock was suddenly wrenched away and scattered by the wind as fiery dust.

The other feature, in the same area, is an earthquake fissure of giant proportions—five miles long and from five to ten feet wide. A tremendous force was required to rip this open, but a force large enough to blow a cubic mile of rock dust into the air could have been responsible. The earth on which we live has been wrenched by many devastating forces generated by volcanoes, earthquakes, wind, and tidal waves. The proportions of the volcanic rings and the earthquake fissure near Cleft prove that two such forces were unleashed in Idaho.

The movement of land along faults is a slow, age-consuming process, so slow that movement along some faults is hardly perceptible during a human lifetime. There are, however, conditions which cause large blocks of rock to shift quite suddenly. Sometimes without warning the earth relieves itself of the terrific strain which has built up within—then there is vast change in the land, some of it resulting in harsh destruction, some in great scenic beauty.

Seattle Earthquake

Although the Pacific Northwest has been singularly spared from disastrous earthquakes, occasionally considerable local damage has resulted from them. Many people in Seattle were just sitting down to lunch, at 11:57, April 13, 1949, when the strongest tremor ever felt in that city caused thousands to forget their hunger and scurry to a place of safety. As the ground rumbled, buildings swayed, and people poured out of offices, there was, for a time, almost panic. The effects of the quake soon made their appearance. Cornices fell from buildings. Fire escapes, loosened from building walls, crashed to the ground.

As the reports of the quake came in, it was found to have affected a large portion of the Pacific Northwest. University of Washington geologists stated that the earthquake had been felt over approximately two hundred thousand square miles—from Vancouver, British Columbia, to Eugene, Oregon, and from Aberdeen, Washington, to the Idaho panhandle. The damage in Seattle was estimated at two million dollars. At Olympia, the imposing new granite and marble capitol, weighing an estimated fifty thousand tons, was badly shaken. Its large chandeliers swayed for fifteen minutes after the quake ended, and all its skylights were shattered, throwing broken glass over the desks in the State Senate and House Chambers. This 1949 quake was the result of the shifting of a fault in the south Olympic Range, ninety miles southwest of Seattle.

Montana Earthquakes

The writings of early-day missionaries and information gained from pioneer newspapers are often the only records available of historic and natural happenings. One such record appears in D. S. Tuttle's book, "Reminiscences of a Missionary Bishop," the story of the first recorded earthquake in Montana:

"On the morning of May 22nd (1869) while we were at breakfast, there came a rumbling sound as of a heavy wagon dragged rapidly across a bridge. With it came a shaking of the house, which threw down pieces of furniture and some dishes in the pantry. The ladies said, 'Some great piece of furniture has fallen somewhere.' I thought one of the large freight wagons in the street which ran close to our front door had by the awkwardness of the driver collided with the corner of our house and shaken it, but going to the door I saw no wagon. Looking upstairs and down, I could find no large piece of furniture that had fallen anywhere. While finishing our breakfast we could only discuss the matter and wonder about it.

"Soon after, I went down Main street and discovered that the same disturbance had been noted everywhere. We were then sure that the town had been visited by an earthquake. About midnight the same day, another shock came. A sudden violent rocking of the rooms and beds was felt by all who were awake. No danger, however, and only very trifling damage was caused either at morning or at night."

Tuttle, without a doubt, experienced a real earthquake. On July 4, 1805, Lewis and Clark heard distant sounds that they could not identify which may have been those of an earthquake. Their diary has this to say about it:

"Since our arrival at the falls (Great Falls of the Missouri) we have repeatedly heard strange noises coming from the mountains in a direction a little north of west. It is heard at different periods of the day and night, sometimes when the air is perfectly still and without a cloud, and consists of one stroke only, or five or six discharges in quick succession. It is loud and resembles precisely the sound of a six-pounder piece of ordnance at the distance of three miles. The Minnetarees frequently mentioned this noise like thunder, which they said the mountains made, but we paid no attention to it, believing it to be some superstition or falsehood. The watermen of the party say that the Pawnees have . . . given the same account of the noise heard in the Black Mountains to the westward of them. The solution of the mystery, given by the philosophy of the watermen, is that it is occasioned by the bursting of the rich mines of silver confined within the bosom of the mountains."

The second earthquake to be recorded in Montana occurred on December 10, 1872. Its epicenter—the earth surface directly above the focus of an earthquake—was about eight miles east of Deer Lodge, near Emery. The "Deer Lodge Independent" of December 14, 1872, states:

"Our valley was given quite a healthy earth shaking which lasted about four seconds . . . The first shock was followed by another on the 11th, between two and three in the morning, which was light, and a third at 6:55, just as the day was breaking. The last one was nearly as heavy as the first. The earth wave which seemed to come from the west, or perhaps a little north of west, was accompanied by a deep rumbling noise, similar to that of a heavily loaded train of cars driven slowly up an ascending grade. The shaking was general throughout the town, and stone, brick, frame and log houses trembled slightly, and the 'chinking' fell from the walls of some of the older houses. There was a general jingling of glassware in the drug store, and the liquid contents . . . slopped up against the sides of the jars like so many little seas in commotion . . .

"There was a general stampede for the open air; men in their shirtsleeves, women with shawls hastily thrown over their heads, frightened children and bewildered Chinamen rushing for the streets . . . The Court House swayed first to the west, and then rocked back and forth until Court, jury and spectators made a complete stampede from the building . . . The shocks were felt at Phillipsburg, Blackfoot, throughout the valley, and in Helena. Eastern and southern Montana seem to have felt none of the shake. The shock was much more distinct in the lowlands than on bench land."

The people of Helena will remember 1935 and 1936 as the years of shaking ground and damage by earthquake to some of their property. A period of shocks began on October 3, 1935, at 7:45 p.m., when a minor tremor was felt. Few paid any attention to the disturbance and no reports of quakes were received from towns near the state capital. On October 12, at 12:51 a.m., a much stronger shock was felt over half the state. Later the fault along which the slippage occurred was found along the south side of Prickly Pear Valley but it was obscured by valley fill, or bottomland sediments, and alluvium. A third earthquake, on October 18, at 9:47 a.m., more severe than those which had already occurred, shook nearly all of Montana, parts of neighboring states to the south, and portions of Canadian provinces to the north. Damage to buildings was extensive. Brick walls collapsed, chimneys came down, tombstones toppled or were rotated counterclockwise. During the last two weeks of October, the earth in Helena vibrated with many minor tremors. People became almost accustomed to the uncertain nature of their landscape. Then on the morning of October 31, the area was again shaken severely. More damage to property occurred—and general anxiety increased.

The experiences and reactions of people are included in the records of most earthquakes. On October 31, a Ten Mile Creek hunter was thrown to his knees. Near Lake Helena, a farmer in an open field heard an ominous rumble, then saw the earth moving in waves. He was thrown to the ground as the earth wave passed. Several other persons in the area reported being struck down by the unsteady ground.

Earthquakes are frequently followed by after-shocks which diminish in intensity as the fault settles into its new position. The damaging quakes at Helena were unusual in that they were preceded by numerous foreshocks, and one of them—on October 12—was severe. Records of the Helena earthquakes, from October 3, 1935, to April 1, 1936, reveal that, during this period, 1,813 quakes occurred, some only minutes apart.

Yellowstone Earthquake

The night of August 17, 1959, was quiet and pleasant in the high country along the Madison River in the Montana Rockies. The moon hung in an almost cloudless sky. Cool mountain air moved among the trees, where numbers of campers had en-joyed the early evening hours around campfires and were now asleep in their tents and trailers.

Just before midnight the quiet northern Rockies roared into life in an earthquake of historic propor-tions. The great range broke along several faults, the earth heaved and tilted, and huge rocks went hurtling down the canyon walls, accumulating in a slide which crossed the valley and came to rest on the opposite side. A section of the mountainside— thirteen hundred feet high and half a mile wide— had broken loose to cause this slide, estimated at eighty million tons. Rock traveled 430 feet up the valley slope opposite. Many sleeping campers died under the rock avalanche. In the narrow canyon, the massive slide generated terrific blasts of air.

Boulders on West Entrance road, five miles from Madison Junction, Yellowstone National Park, a result of the 1959 Madison River earthquake. Notice the trees felled by rolling rock.

One man was seen clinging to a small tree in a tornado-like wind. Several persons had their clothes torn from their bodies.

Highway engineers and rescue crews faced grave problems. Injured tourists had to be evacuated. Communications had to be re-established. Rock was four hundred feet deep on U. S. Highway 287 in the canyon, and other sections of the road had been wrenched out of line to make them impassable. The Madison River had been dammed and water was rising rapidly behind the slide. Eventually the water

Photo No. 69   *National Park Service*

Earthquake-caused slide blocking highway south of Golden Gate viaduct, Yellowstone National Park. The closely-jointed character of the rock at this point was one reason why this great volume of rock was loosened by the strong quake of 1959.

became 180 feet deep in the gorge. Six miles up-stream, the Hebgen Dam had been cracked and otherwise damaged. Here was more tragedy in the making. Should this dam give way, water would race downstream over the earthquake slide, then on to Ennis and ranches and resorts beyond.

It was decided to cut a fifty-foot ditch in the slide, lessening the grade at the outlet and providing more room for water to escape before a washout of the slide or of Hebgen Dam occurred. Earth-moving machines worked day and night to move a vast quantity of debris. The job was finished on November 1 of that year, 1959.

Yellowstone National Park, twenty miles east of the Madison disaster, literally jumped when the quake struck along the Madison. Buildings were wrenched from their foundations and swayed under the impact. Boulders rolled down mountain sides onto highways and even into buildings. (Photos Nos. 68, 69, and 70). At Old Faithful Inn, the chimney collapsed into the dining room. Had the quake struck during daylight hours, the casualty list would have been much greater.

Visitors to the geyser basin at Yellowstone, find that this area has several interesting features because of these massive convulsions within the earth. At the outset of the quake, most of the geysers erupted simultaneously. Daylight revealed that, during the night, hot water had been violently thrown about in the geyser basin. Well-known geysers such as Castle, Daisy, and Great Fountain thereafter erupted oftener. Clepsydra, which, prior to the quake, had erupted in four-day intervals, now erupted continuously, forcing out vast amounts of steam. Economic Geyser, dormant for twenty-five years, became active every thirty minutes. Giantess Geyser blew water two hundred feet into the air for four days. Grand Geyser—one of the older, more dependable geysers—stopped performing, whereas Earthquake Geyser, a newcomer, began spouting seventy-five to a hundred feet high. Some quiet, hot-water pools suddenly became roaring giants. Sapphire Pool in Biscuit Basin, known to thousands of tourists, waited three weeks, then blew up with tremendous force. It erupted regularly for eight weeks, then a tremor stopped it. Sixteen days later a new quake triggered it into action again (Photos Nos.

Photo No. 70   *National Park Service*

Fissure near Firehole Lake, Yellowstone National Park, showing colossal force of the
1959 earthquake.

Photo No. 71   *National Park Service*

Morning Geyser in action—one of several whose eruption schedule was altered by the 1959 earthquake. Eruptions began averaging four hours apart as compared with one daily morning eruption prior to the earthquake.

71 and 72). Here in Montana, earth's quaking gave rise not only to a cataclysmic destruction but also to a huge water carnival of spectacular beauty.

Earth scientists say that the Montana quakes prove that the Rocky Mountains are still growing. The Madison Range, which began rising from the sea fifty million years ago, is still rising and buckling, pushed upward by the unfathomable forces at work within the earth. When the upper layers of rock can no longer resist the forces below them, they

Photo No. 72   *National Park Service*

Unusual turbulence in Silex Spring, in Lower Geyser Basin, Yellowstone National Park. Many hot springs as well as geysers showed changes in behavior after the 1959 earthquake. Within a week some had begun to return to normal, but many changes have persisted.

break along a fault. Events like those at Madison River and in Yellowstone Park are then repeated.

Oregon Earthquakes

Records show that no disastrous earthquakes have occurred in Oregon. The state has well-kept registers of its many minor temblors though, most recent of which took place on November 6, 1961, when Portland and its environs shuddered — and quaked a bit. This temblor, which shook an area from Hood River to Tillamook and from St. Helens to Salem, was caused by sudden earth movement along a deep 150-mile-long fault, twenty miles west of Portland. Seismologists who have been watching this fault for the past eight years report that the shock, on November 6, was no stronger than others which have occurred along it. Damage from it could be given nuisance status only: walls were cracked, lights broken, wall plaster cracked, and grocery items spilled from shelves. For a moment the ground shivered crazily.

The writer has been unable to learn of a single life lost in Oregon from earthquakes. Records show that California has experienced more quakes than Washington and that Oregon has had fewer than Washington. Between 1866 and 1949, Oregon had only four quakes with an intensity great enough to damage masonry and chimneys. This does not mean that Oregon is an area immune from violent shocks. Considering the length of time that earthquakes have been shaking the world, man's records can be considered only as fragments.

Records of the characteristics and damage of earthquakes are carefully prepared. These records are then consulted when a large building or a dam is to be constructed in an area where have occurred earthquakes strong enough to cause structural failure. Engineers design their projects accordingly.

Earth Shocks and Their Work

Most earthquakes are caused by the slippage of rock masses along fault planes but, since an earthquake is simply a shaking or vibration of the ground, there are other causes for this form of earth disturbance. The volcano, as it coughs and erupts its molten rock, causes the earth to quake. In fact, some of the world's great earthquakes have been set off by the volcanoes. For minor quakes, earth slides and rock slides have often been responsible. Ice and snow avalanches also shake the ground around them.

Many persons believe that these temblors are rare occurrences because only those of considerable intensity make news of national or world importance. Though the small tremor has only local importance, it is the minor, harmless shivers running through the earth's layers that build up the impressive total happening around the world every day. The old earth on which we live has been setting its restless surface trembling ever since it began—and the end of its quaking is not yet in sight. In an ordinary year—and felt over a fairly wide area—we may expect one great earthquake, ten major earthquakes, one hundred destructive shocks, one thousand damaging shocks, ten thousand minor strong shocks, and one hundred thousand tremors.

Earthquakes occur oftener at some places than at others, but quakes of varying intensity may happen anywhere on the surface of the globe—and in rock underlying the sea as well. The areas which girdle the Pacific Ocean are shaken by eighty per cent of these temblors. Another earthquake belt starts in the Mediterranean area and extends eastward across Asia. This region experiences fifteen per cent of the earth's annual quakes.

No one knows when quiet areas will receive a strong shock. We have learned to predict the weather quite accurately but have yet to make a good start in the prediction of earthquakes. However, we have learned this: any area which has once experienced an earthquake may expect another. Forces which ultimately cause the earth to tremble are continually at work. When immense weight, prompted by impossible strain, must adjust itself, then somewhere in the area lies the fault—polished, inclined, and ready to allow the necessary slippage. The magnitude of the forces developing mysteriously within the rock masses of the earth remains a mystery, as does the moment when these forces will snap, causing the earth to tremble.

The effects of a quake are diverse. The shaking often causes both earth and rock perched on mountain sides to rumble downhill, creating minor tremors along their course. Roads and fences are occasionally torn out of line, sometimes as much as several feet. Bottom mud flows resulting from earthquakes have been known to alter the depth of bays and inlets. In 1889, the floor of Yakutat Bay, in Alaska, rose fifty feet because of an earthquake. Submarine cables have been snapped by the movement of such bottom materials.

Though there is no way to determine the approach of an earthquake, there is an instrument to determine its whereabouts and its intensity. This is the seismograph. By sinking a metal shaft deep into the earth, to bedrock if possible, the vibration of the earth can be captured and transferred, by means of an inked stylus, to a paper-covered cylinder turned by clockwork. So sensitively can the seismograph be constructed that explosions, heavy vehicles, and distant earthquakes will leave their wavy-line story as the recording needle swings to and fro. When earthquakes occur, the earth actually ripples in waves, and many of these waves travel around the world. In 1953, at Kamchatka Peninsula— where earthquakes seem to happen regularly — a tremendous quake sent waves across the globe to waiting seismographs in New York. There the waves were estimated to have the thickness of a half dollar.

Like other major phenomena, earthquake lore has many superstitions and old wives' tales mingled with the facts. This is understandable. The terrifying moment of an earth shock is not a time for widespread composure. What is seen and heard is apt to be distorted by fear. There are often reports of sparks, smoke, and even fire coming from cracks opened by the force of earthquakes. That these events are generally short circuits, resulting from broken electrical installations, is usually not realized.

Some tell of earthquake weather, a sort of close, ominous silence before the shock occurs. This might be, but more likely the day just happened to be quiet and sultry before the quake. Then there is the well-known story of deep cracks which suddenly open in the earth, only to close with equal suddenness, swallowing people and objects. These tales are only half true. Cracks do open in the ground but they do not close by earthquake action; they may partly fill by cave-in. Should a person fall into such a crack during an earthquake, he would be greatly frightened, his clothes would be badly soiled, and parts of his body might be bruised, but, unless he had received broken limbs, he would be able to crawl out to see how the earthquake was progressing—and to examine land form changes wrought by the earth's convulsions.

GLOSSARY

Aa—Extremely rough, viscous lava found on the surface of a slow-moving flow. Aa hardens into a distorted, jumbled surface. The word is Hawaiian in origin.

Aftershock—An earthquake shock of lesser intensity following the main or more severe shock.

Agate—A waxy-appearing quartz in which color occurs in bands or groups.

Agglomerate—A rock containing angular, cemented particles. A volcanic breccia.

Algae—Members of the simplest division of plants having no leaves, roots or stems. Algae absorb food from water.

Alpine glacier—A glacier lying in the summit area of a high mountain.

Andesite—An extrusive, gray igneous rock consisting chiefly of acid plagioclase feldspar. The word comes from the Andes Mountains.

Antecedent stream—A stream which continues in its course although the area in which it flows is uplifted.

Archeology—The study of past human life as revealed through relics, artifacts and homesites.

Argillite—A compressed shale containing considerable clay.

Basalt—A dark, fine-grained, igneous rock containing large amounts of ferromagnesian minerals. The lava flows of the Columbia Plateau in Washington, Idaho, and Oregon are composed of basalt.

Batholith—The largest kind of intrusive igneous rock. The sides of a batholith flare outward as they proceed downward. Batholiths generally are thought to extend downward several miles and by some are considered to be bottomless.

Bedding plane—Where sedimentary rocks are separated into layers.

Block mountains—Mountains formed when great blocks of mountains are dropped or uplifted by faulting.

Blowout—A hollow blown out by the wind in an area of sand deposits.

Brachiopod—A bivalved sea animal having shell valves of unequal size.

Breccia—Cemented, angular particles of rock.

Bryozoan—A sea animal having a branched or moss-like appearance. Bryozoans reproduce by budding.

Caldera—A large volcanic crater which is much wider than it is deep, and is caused by an explosion or the collapse of the crater.

Chimney island—See "sea stack."

Cinder cone—Volcanic cone made when exploded cinder particles are deposited in a circular mound around the crater.

Cirque—An amphitheater-like depression at high elevations in mountain regions, formed by the plucking action of glacial ice. Cirques mark the places where valley glaciers are born.

Columnar structure—Columns of rock, usually six-sided, and caused by molten rock contracting at equally-spaced intervals. Columnar structure has much the same patterns as the cracks found on dried mud flats.

Concretion—Semi-rounded masses of rock deposited in cavities in limestone by calcium-laden water.

Conglomerate—Rock consisting of cemented, rounded rock particles, ranging in size from pebbles to boulders.

Continental glacier—A glacier covering continental areas.

Contour lines—The lines of a topographic map on which points having the same elevation are shown.

Coral—The calcareous skeleton of a branched sea animal. Openings through which the animal takes in food are found along its stem-like structure.

Crevasse—A deep crack or fissure in glacial ice.

Crinoid—A lily-shaped sea animal constructed much like a plant, with five or more feathery "petals" or arms.

Crystal—In geology, a mineral having a unique atom arrangement, resulting in a plane-sided structure. Crystals are identified by the position of the planes which make up the outer surfaces.

Delta—Accumulated sediments brought to quiet water by a stream. This, in time, results in new land being formed at the mouth of the stream.

Dike—A vertical or near-vertical, tabular, intruded igneous mass of rock.

Diorite—A coarse-grained rock containing plagioclase feldspar and one or more ferromagnesian minerals.

Drumlin—An elongated mound, usually 25 to 150 feet high, formed as sediment under a glacier. The longest axis of a drumlin is parallel to the direction in which the glacier moved.

Dune—A hill formed by wind-deposited sand.

Earthquake fissure—A crack in the crust of the earth caused by an earthquake.

Embayment—An indentation in a coastline containing a bay.

Eon—An immeasurably long period of time; also, any of the grand divisions of geologic time.

Epoch—One division of geologic time; a division of a period. In turn, a period is a division of an era.

Epicenter—The point directly above an earthquake disturbance.

Era—One of the major divisions of geologic time; as, the Paleozoic era.

Erosion—The abrasion or wearing away of land by water, glaciers, waves, or wind.

Erratic—A piece of rock, large or small, of different composition from the land surface upon which it rests. Erratics are usually transported by glaciers or river bergs.

Escarpment—The long, steep face of a rock exposure, such as a cliff. Also the steep face of a terrace.

Exfoliation—The process by which some rocks are weathered from surface flaking due to the corrosive action of earth chemicals and the contraction and expansion of heat and cold.

Fault—A crack or fracture in the earth's crust along which movement has occurred.

Fiord—A partly-submerged glacial trough extending into the sea.

Fissure—A crack or parting of a rock formation; usually a large, extended fracture.

Foreshock—An earthquake shock which precedes the shock of greatest intensity.

Formation—A layer or series of bedded rock having characteristics that set it apart from other rock masses.

Fossil—The mold, cast, imprint or remains of a plant or animal preserved in rock.

Fumerole—A place from which earth gases escape. Fumeroles are characteristic of regions once having had volcanic activity, and of regions where underground molten rock has solidified just under the surface.

Gastropod—A marine animal having a univalve shell, such as a snail.

Geology—The science which treats of the history of the earth and its life, especially as recorded in the rocks.

Geyser—Intermittent spring from which hot water and steam are ejected under pressure.

Glacial striations—Grooves or scratches on rock, made by glacier-carried rock which is dragged over the rock surfaces.

Glaciation—Erosion action of glaciers.

Glacier—A thick sheet of ice moving over extensive areas of earth.

Gneiss—A metamorphic rock having a roughly-foliated, coarse textured character. Gneiss is alternately banded with minerals of unlike kinds.

Graben—A valley caused by sinking of the earth due to faulting.

Granitic rock—Intrusive, coarse-grained rock containing orthoclase feldspar, quartz, and a ferromagnesian mineral.

Graptolite—A marine animal having a stem or stalk at the top of which are numerous fine branches that, in fossil form, look like pencil lines.

Habitat—A place where a plant or an animal thrives; the natural abode of a plant or an animal.

Hanging valley—A valley whose mouth is higher than the valley of which it is a tributary. Waterfalls often fall from hanging valleys into the trunk or main river.

Headland—A promontory or cape extending into the sea.

Ice cave—A cave in which underground water freezes into ice. Insulated by rock from summer heat, underground ice often persists the year round.

Icefall—Glacial ice falling down the steep face of a cliff to re-form at the bottom.

Igneous rock—Solidified, once-molten rock.

Interglacial period—The period of time between glacial activity. If more glacial periods lie ahead for the earth, the present time may be considered an interglacial period.

Intermittent stream—A stream whose flow occurs only after a rain or when snow melts.

Intermontane—Between mountains.

Intruded rock—Rock which has consolidated from magma underground. This rock often intrudes in cracks and weaker zones in rock-forming dikes and sills.

Kettle—A rounded depression in glacial material caused when a great mass of ice, lodged in the material under a glacier, melts. Kettles are created only when a glacier ceases to move.

Lateral moraine—A moraine formed along the sides of a valley glacier from rock fragments gathered along the valley wall and from material which falls to the ice from upper exposed slopes.

Lava—Fluid rock which reaches the surface of the earth through a fissure in the earth or from a volcano.

Lava bomb—A molten lump of lava, blown from a volcano, which solidifies in the air before striking the ground.

Lava cave—A cave formed when molten lava flows out from under an already solidified crust.

Lava dome—Some lava which wells up from fissures in the earth is too viscous to flow readily. The rounded dome which results is called a lava dome.

Lava flood—A sheet-like flow or flood of melted rock upon the earth's surface. The Columbia Plateau was built when a series of liquid sheets of molten basalt flooded this area.

Leeward—The direction toward which the wind blows; or, pertaining to the sheltered side of a windy area.

Limestone—A rock formed from shells and skeletal remains of sea animals which have built their solid parts from calcium carbonate.

Littoral current—The current of water which parallels a coastline.

Loess—Yellowish-brown loam earth found in some places in the Pacific Northwest. It is unstratified and is thought to be wind deposited.

Magma—Molten rock found within the earth's surface. Igneous rock is formed when magma solidifies.

Mammoth—An extinct elephant whose molar teeth had a cement filling between the enamel ridges. Mammoths also had curving tusks and a hairy coat.

Marble—A metamorphic rock consisting of recrystallized limestone (calcium carbonate).

Mastodon—A prehistoric elephant differing from the mammoth and other elephants in its molar teeth, which have conical projections.

Matterhorn—A pyramid-like peak formed when several cirque walls meet or intersect, resulting in a steep, sharp peak. This word takes its name from the famous Matterhorn in the Swiss Alps, which is a model for this kind of peak.

Metamorphic rock—A rock altered by heat, pressure, or chemical action.

Meteorology—The science concerned with the study of the atmosphere and used in the analysis and prediction of weather.

Mineral—A natural substance which has a characteristic internal structure, chemical composition, and physical property.

Mollusk—A kind of shellfish, of which there are many; as, clams, oysters, and other mussels, having a soft body protected by a calcareous shell.

Monadnock—A large rock mass standing as an erosional remnant. Sharp hills or upright rock formations are sometimes found as monadnocks on peneplains.

Moraine—Accumulation of rock debris deposited by a glacier.

Neve—Granulated ice made from snow. Neve ice, when solidified, forms the ice found in glaciers.

Obsidian—Glassy volcanic rock caused by rapid cooling of molten rock. This rock is common among the lava flows of the Columbia Plateau, where molten basalt encountered ponds and streams.

Outcrop—A surface-appearing rock or formation.

Oxbow lake—The lake which results when a crescent-shaped portion of a meandering river has been cut off.

Pahoehoe—Lava which has hardened into a smooth, ropy surface, often glistening in appearance.

Paleontology—The science dealing with the life–both plant and animal–of past geologic ages.

Parasitic cone—A smaller cone on the side of a larger cone.

Pelecypod—A two-shelled sea animal having a hatchet-shaped foot which distinguishes it from other members of its family group, the gastropods.

Peneplain—An eroded, nearly-flat land surface which has almost reached sea level.

Peneplaining cycle—The cycle through which land forms pass from their original elevations to final leveling by erosion.

Period—A division of geologic time longer than an epoch and included in an era; as, the Devonian period.

Petrify—To change organic matter into stone.

Physiography—The science dealing with the nature and formation of the earth's crust.

Pillow lava—Lava having rounded, pillow-shaped structure because of its extrusion under water.

Plateau—A tableland or plain found at high elevation. The Columbia Plateau, in the Pacific Northwest, is one of the largest in the world.

Playa—A desert basin lake in which water is held seasonally or temporarily.

Plunge pool—A round hole excavated by water descending over a fall.

Porphyry—A rock in which crystals, called phenocrysts, large enough to be seen by the naked eye, are surrounded by a fine-grained, ground mass.

Pothole—Cylindrical hole in a river or stream bottom, ground by water carrying rock fragments.

Print—An impression made in rock by some form of prehistoric life, such as a leaf.

Pumice—A volcanic rock having a foam-like, glassy texture. Numerous air spaces in this rock allow it to float on water.

Quartzite—A metamorphic sandstone whose quartz particles have become so thoroughly cemented that the individual grains cannot be distinguished.

Rejuvenated river—A river whose normal progression through youth, maturity, and old age has been interrupted by uplift, causing it again to exhibit more youthful characteristics.

Rhyolite—An extrusive igneous rock consisting of small glassy particles.

Rift—A valley formed by the sinking of a block-like portion of the land between two parallel faults. Sometimes called a graben.

Ripple marks—Washboard-like sandy waves found on the bottom of some streams, lakes, and oceans, caused by water currents or waves.

River berg—A large mass of ice floated by a river. At the close of the ice age, large masses of ice, broken from adjacent glaciers, floated down the Columbia River.

River maturity—Pertaining to a river which has adopted a meandering pattern and flows through a subdued landscape which the river and its tributaries have thoroughly eroded and dissected.

River piracy—The capture of a part of the headwaters of a stream by another stream which has eaten its way across a divide from a neighboring valley.

Rock—A piece of the earth's crust consisting of one mineral or several consolidated minerals.

Sand lake—A lake cupped in sand. Ocean waves sometimes throw sand bars across the mouths of streams, causing lakes to form.

Sandspit—A sandy, finger-like land form extending into a body of water from a promontory.

Sandstone—A rock composed of rock and mineral particles cemented together. Quartz particles are common in sandstone.

Saturation zone—The part of the earth, below the water table (or upper surface of ground water), which is saturated.

Scaphopod—A marine mollusk having a tapered tube-like shell, open at both ends, and a pointed foot for burrowing.

Scoria—Cinder-like lava ejected by a volcano.

Sea cave—A cave on the ocean shoreline excavated by ocean waves.

Sea stack—A land remnant found along coastlines, the result of wave erosion. Sea stacks are often nothing but sharp pinnacles rising from the water. Sometimes called "chimney islands."

Sedimentary rock—Rock formed by earth materials deposited in lakes and oceans.

Seismograph—An instrument used in detecting and measuring earth shocks. A metal shaft is sunk to bedrock if possible. When the earth shocks occur, an inked stylus records the vibrations of the earth on paper on a revolving drum.

Serac—Jagged ice surface produced by irregular melting of the surface of a glacier by sun and dry wind.

Serrated ridge—A sharp, notched mountain ridge, the result of severe erosion.

Shale—A rock found in layers formed from compact mud or clay.

Shield volcano—A volcano built by successive, overlapping flows of basalt lava.

Silica—A stony substance consisting of silicon dioxide. Quartz is a common silica mineral.

Silt—Fine sedimentary material carried by running water.

Siltstone—A rock formed from silt.

Slate—A thin sheet of black rock, resulting from metamorphic forces acting on shale.

Spa—A mineral spring.

Spatter cone—A volcanic cone made by liquid masses of rock spattering around the volcanic vent.

Spouting horn—A horn-shaped tunnel in rock, up which water is driven by waves. Water is forced to spout from a surface opening in the rock.

Stalactite—An icicle-like deposit of calcium carbonate suspended from the roof of a cave.

Stalagmite—A deposit similar to a stalactite but formed on the floor of a cavern by dripping water which contains calcium carbonate.

Stratum—A layer of rock or earth in a bedded position; often interbedded between other layers of similar or different character.

Striation—A groove or scratch in a rock surface produced by scouring of rock-laden ice.

Structural depression—A depressed area in the earth's surface caused by down-warping or faulting of the land.

Subterranean—Pertaining to the regions within the earth.

Subterranean conduit—A natural underground channel through which subterranean water is piped.

Talus—Rock fragments which collect in a sloping deposit at the foot of a cliff.

Temblor—An earthquake.

Temperate marine climate—A climate characterized by cool summers and mild winters, typical of the Pacific Northwest coastal area.

Terminal moraine—Unsorted earth materials found pushed out in front of the lower end of a glacier.

Terrace—A landform having a level top bordered by a steep-sided bank or escarpment. The terraces in the Okanogan Valley of Washington have these features.

Till—Unsorted glacially-deposited material consisting of sand, clay, gravel, and boulders.

Topography—Relief of land surface, with the positions and elevations of its land forms.

Topographic map—A map on which the relief of an era is shown by means of contour lines.

Transpiration—The outward passage of water vapor through the pores in leaves. Tree leaves, in summer, exhale great quantities of water.

Trashy fallow—Cultivation of land by means of a steel bar which stirs the soil below the surface, leaving the topside stubble in a standing position so as to bind the soil and thus prevent erosion.

Tree mold—The mold made when a tree becomes encased in molten lava. The mold results when the wood burns away, leaving a cylindrical mold of solidified rock.

Tremor—A trembling of the earth's crust by earthquake vibrations.

Trilobite—An extinct arthropod having a divided, furrowed, and segmented body, which divides into three parts.

Truncated spur—The cutoff end of a tributary ridge; the result of a glacier's having worn off the end of a ridge as it enlarged a valley. Truncated spurs are usually triangular in shape.

Tuff—Fine, solidified volcanic ash.

Valley fill—Valley sediments, glacial or alluvial, partially filling a valley.

Valley glacier—A glacier which occupies a mountain valley.

Vertebrate—An animal having a backbone.

Volcanic bomb—A mass of volcanic matter flung into the air —often for a considerable distance—and solidifying to an almost sphere-like chunk.

Volcanic plug—A somewhat cylindrical mass of volcanic rock which has solidified in the vent of a non-active volcano.

Volcano—A high, often cone-shaped mountain built from subterranean molten rock blown from a vent in the earth.

Water table—The top surface of the saturation zone.

Windward—The point or side from which the wind blows.

GEOLOGIC CHART

Geologic Era	Geologic Epoch	Age in Years	GEOLOGIC EVENTS
CENOZOIC ERA —The Age of Mammals—	**Quaternary** (Recent)	(25,000)	Extensive glaciation in Puget Sound area and in the Cascade Mountains of Washington and Oregon. Also in the Rocky Mountains.
	Pleistocene or Glacial Epoch	2,000,000	Cascade Mountain volcanoes active. Volcanism in Idaho. Extinction of large mammals such as the prehistoric elephant.
	Tertiary Pliocene Epoch	12,000,000	High Cascades of Oregon erected. Rocky Mountains gain maximum height. Cooling climate. Arrival of man. Continued volcanism. Uplift of Olympic Mountains. Local basins along Pacific Coast receive sediments.
	Miocene Epoch	30,000,000	Rocky Mountains rejuvenated by uplift at close of Miocene. Extensive faulting begins in the Great Basin. This has persisted to the present. Colossal lava flooding of the Columbia Plateau and Snake River Valley. Cascade Mountains emerge—growth continues through Pliocene and Pleistocene. Growth of Cascades causes arid climate east of these mountains. First Olympic Mountains uplifted. Rocky Mountains peneplained at beginning of Miocene.
	Oligocene Epoch	40,000,000	Thick sediments laid down in Cape Flattery, Washington, area. John Day Basin filled with volcanic ash. Magnolia, cycads and fig trees grow in Yukon area of Alaska. This period leaves one of the richest known deposits of Cenozoic mammals, in John Day Basin.
	Eocene Epoch	55,000,000	Rocky Mountains eroded. Extensive s e d i m e n t a t i o n in the Puget Sound area. Coal formed in Puget Sound area. Basalt flows in Western Washington and Oregon covered larger area than New England. Glacial weather in Rocky Mountains followed by warm cycle. Sea-floor volcanic eruptions in Olympic Mountains area.
	Paleocene Epoch	60,000,000	North America emerges into approximately p r e s e n t size and shape. Sea inundates western Washington. General erosion of uplifted areas.

MESOZOIC ERA —The Age of Reptiles—	Upper Cretaceous Period	130,000,000	Rocky Mountains completed at end of Cretaceous. Central Idaho batholith intruded. (16,000 square miles in area.) Boulder batholith intruded. (Contained extensive copper deposits, underlying Butte, Montana area.) Cretaceous sedimentary beds deposited along the Pacific Coast from Alaska to Vancouver Island.
	Lower Cretaceous Period		Greatest flooding of geologic time. Modern deciduous trees develop in mild climate to dominate landscape.
	Jurassic Period	168,000,000	Flooding of Rocky Mountain region. Evergreen forests and first birds appear during mild, humid climate.
	Triassic Period	200,000,000	Dinosaurs prominent. Triassic sediments deposited in Idaho and Wyoming. Much of the Pacific Northwest flooded. Limestone deposited in Alaska.
PALEOZOIC ERA	Permian Period	235,000,000	Volcanics of Pacific border, in Alaska. Wide-spread deserts in Great Basin. Coal-forming vegetation disappears. Numerous reptiles develop.
The Age of Amphibians	Pennsyl- vanian Period	315,000,000	Some inundation of Pacific Northwest in middle of period. Age of large insects. Amphibians flourish.
	Missis- sippian Period	330,000,000	Limestone 1200 feet thick deposited in Yellowstone National Park. All of North America elevated, extensive erosion.
The Age of Fishes	Devonian Period	350,000,000	Devonian period not well known in the West. Devonian limestone in Canadian Rockies. First forests and amphibians appear. Aquatic vertebrates develop.
	Silurian Period	375,000,000	Parts of Idaho and Montana flooded but no submergence in most of Pacific Northwest. First appearance of air-breathing animals. (No mountains in America at close of period.)
The Age of Invertebrates	Ordovician Period	445,000,000	Slight emergence of flooded areas and further intermittent flooding. Dolomite found in Montana and Arctic Canada. Primitive fishes and gastropods develop.
	Cambrian Period	550,000,000	Inland seas form in Rocky Mountain region. Seas swarm with invertebrates. No land animals yet. Seaweeds. No woody plants.

BIBLIOGRAPHY

Atwood, Wallace W. *The Physiographic Provinces of North America.* Boston: Ginn, 1940.

Blackwelder, Eliot, and Harlan Barrows. *Elements of Geology.* New York: American Book, 1911.

Bretz, J. Harlan. "Pleistocene of Western Washington." *American Geological Society Proceedings.* New York: 1915.

—— "The Grand Coulee, Washington." *American Geological Society Special Publication.* New York: 1932.

—— "Channeled Scabland of Eastern Washington." *Geographical Review.* Vol. 18, pp. 446-477. New York: 1928.

—— "Washington's Channeled Scabland." *Division of Mines and Geology Bulletin No. 45.* Olympia, Washington: April 15, 1959.

Brockman, C. Frank. *The Story of the Petrified Forest.* Tacoma, Washington: Pacific Bank Note Co.: 1954.

Brooks, James E., Editor. *Oregon Almanac and Book of Facts, 1961-62.* Portland, Oregon: Binfords & Mort, 1961.

Campbell, C. D. "Washington Geology and Resources." *Research Studies of the State College of Washington.* Vol. XXI, No. 2. Pullman, Washington: State College of Washington, June, 1953.

Case, Robert Ormond, and Victoria Case. *Last Mountains, the Story of the Cascades.* Portland, Oregon: Binfords & Mort, 1956.

Chapell, Walter M. "Glaciation of Columbia Valley in the Wenatchee-Chelan District." *American Geological Society Proceedings*, p. 344. New York: 1936.

Cloos, Hans. *Conversation with the Earth.* New York: Knopf, 1959.

Condon, Thomas. *Oregon Geology.* Portland, Oregon: Gill, 1910.

Cotton, C A. *Geomorphology of New Zealand* (Part I, Systematic). Wellington, N. Z.: Dominion Museum, 1926.

BIBLIOGRAPHY

Culver, Harold E. "The Geology of Washington." *Department of Conservation and Development Bulletin No. 32.* Olympia, Washington: 1936.

Danner, Wilbert R. *Geology of Olympic National Park.* Seattle, Washington: University of Washington, 1955.

Davis, William M. "The Mission Range, Montana." *Geographical Review,* Vol. 2, pp. 267-288. New York: 1916.

Douglas, William O. *My Wilderness.* New York: Doubleday, 1960.

Emmons, William H., Ira S. Allison, Clinton R. Stauffer, and George A. Thiel. *Geology: Principles and Processes.* New York: McGraw-Hill, 1960.

Fennemen, Nevin M. *Physiography of Western United States.* New York: McGraw-Hill, 1931.

Fenton, C. L., and M. A. Fenton. *Rocks and Their Stories.* New York: Doubleday, 1951.

Flint, Richard F. *Glacial and Pleistocene Geology.* New York: John Wiley, 1957.

Freeman, Otis W., and Howard H. Martin. *The Pacific Northwest.* New York: John Wiley, 1954.

Fuller, George W. *A History of the Pacific Northwest.* New York: Knopf, 1947.

Glassley, Ray H. *Visit the Pacific Northwest.* Portland, Oregon: Binfords & Mort, 1948.

Grater, Russell K. *Grater's Guide to Mount Rainier National Park.* Portland, Oregon. Binfords & Mort, 1954.

Hamilton, James McClellan. *From Wilderness to Statehood—A History of Montana.* Portland, Oregon: Binfords & Mort, 1957.

Hinds, Norman E. A. *Geomorphology, the Evolution of Landscape.* New York: Prentice-Hall, 1943.

Holmes, Chauncey W. *Introduction to College Geology.* New York: Macmillan, 1949.

Hulley, Clarence C. *Alaska: Past and Present.* Portland, Oregon: Binfords & Mort, 1958.

Hult, Ruby El. *Untamed Olympics: The Story of a Peninsula.* Portland, Oregon: Binfords & Mort, 1956.

Idaho: A Guide in Word and Picture. American Guide Series. Caldwell, Idaho: Caxton, 1950.

Jones, Fred O. *Grand Coulee from Hell to Breakfast.* Portland, Oregon: Binfords & Mort, 1947.

Lahee, Frederic H. *Field Geology.* New York: McGraw-Hill, 1931.

—— "Lava River Caves in Oregon." *Oregon State Highway Department.* Salem, Oregon, 1955.

[295]

Livingston, Vaughn E. *Fossils in Washington.* Olympia, Washington: State Printing Office, 1959.

Lobeck, Armin K. *Things Maps Don't Tell Us.* New York: Macmillan, 1958.

Longwell, Chester R., Adolph Knopf and Richard F. Flint. *A Textbook of Geology.* (Part I, Physical Geology). New York: John Wiley, 1932.

McArthur, Lewis A. *Oregon Geographic Names.* Portland, Oregon: Binfords & Mort, 1952.

McMachen, Joseph G. "Grand Coulee of Washington." Address before Northwestern Scientific Association. Spokane, Washington: 1928.

McNeil, Fred H. *Wy'east, The Mountain.* Portland, Oregon: Metropolitan, 1937.

Mackin, J. Hoover. "Eastern Margin of the Puget Sound Lobe." *American Geological Society.* New York: 1937.

Meany, Edmond S. *Mount Rainier, A Record of Exploration.* Portland, Oregon: Binfords & Mort, 1953.

Meinzer, Oscar Edward. "The Glacial History of the Columbia in the Big Bend Region, Washington." *Academy of Science Journal,* Vol. 8, pp. 411-412. New York: June, 1918.

Montana Almanac, 1959-60. Missoula, Montana: Montana State University, 1958.

Mount Hood. American Guide Series. New York: Duell, Sloan & Pearce, 1940.

Oregon: End of the Trail. American Guide Series. Portland Oregon: Binfords & Mort, 1951.

Pardee, Joseph T. "Unusual Currents in Glacial Lake, Missoula, Montana." *American Geological Society Bulletin,* Vol. 53, pp. 1569-1600. New York: November, 1942.

Pauli, Wolfgang F. *The World of Life.* Boston: Houghton Mifflin, 1949.

Pearl, Richard M. *How to Know the Minerals and Rocks.* New York: McGraw-Hill, 1949.

Pirsson, Louis V. *A Textbook of Geology* (Part I, Physical Geology). New York: John Wiley, 1929.

Rhodenbaugh, Edward F. *Sketches of Idaho Geology.* Boise, Idaho: Caxton, 1961.

Russell, I. C. *Rivers of North America.* New York: Putnam, 1907.

Schuchert, Charles, and Carl O. Dunbar. *A Textbook of Geology* (Part II, Historical Geology). New York: John Wiley, 1933.

Scott, William Berryman. *An Introduction to Geology.* New York: Macmillan, 1932.

BIBLIOGRAPHY

Shimer, Hervey W., and Robert R. Shrock. *Index Fossils of North America.* New York: John Wiley, 1944.

Shuler, Ellis W. *Rocks and Rivers of America.* New York: Ronald, 1945.

Smith, Warren D. *The Scenic Treasure House of Oregon.* Portland, Oregon: Binfords & Mort, 1941.

Stevenson, Elmo. *Nature Rambles in the Wallowas.* Portland, Oregon: Metropolitan, 1938.

Von Bernewitz, M. W. *Handbook for Prospectors.* New York: McGraw-Hill, 1931.

Washington: A Guide to the Evergreen State. American Guide Series. Portland, Oregon: Binfords & Mort, 1950.

Williams, Howell. *Crater Lake, the Story of its Origin.* Berkeley and Los Angeles, California: University of California, 1957.

—— "Volcanoes of the Three Sisters Region, Oregon Cascades." *Bulletin of the Department of Geological Sciences,* Vol. 27. Berkeley, California: University of California, June, 1944.

Willis, Bailey. "Changes in River Courses in Washington Territory Due to Glaciation." *United States Geologic Survey Bulletin No. 40.* Washington, D.C.: April, 1887.

Zim, Herbert S., Paul R. Shaffer and Raymond Perlman. *Rocks and Minerals.* New York: Golden, 1957.

INDEX

A

B

SCENIC GEOLOGY

Bonneville Dam, 186
Borax Lakes, 246
Bottom mud flows, 280
Boulder Creek, Washington, 110
Brachiopods, 119, 120
Bremerton, Washington 128
Bretz, J. Harlan, 61
Brewster, Washington, 72
British Admiralty, 146
British Columbia, 14, 45, 106, 185
  fiords, 230
  plateau, 15
Brogan, Phil F., 158
Broken Top, Three Sisters, Oregon, 159
Brookings, Oregon, 228
Brookings Terrace, Oregon, 228
Broughton, Lt. William R., 145-6
Bryozoans, 119, 120
Buffalo Eddy, Snake River, 201
Buhl, Idaho, 211
Bunyan, Paul, 44
Burley, Idaho, 248
Burns, Oregon, 245, 246
Butte, Montana, 54

C

Cabinet Mountains, 57
Caldera, 74, 75, 152, 154, 155
Caldron, 180
California Road, 248
Cambrian, 119, 120
Canada, 186
Canadian Rockies, 185
Canadian Shield, Manitoba, 31
Cannon Beach, Oregon, 220
Cape Blanco, 96, 229
  terrace, 229
Cape Heceta, Oregon, 223
Cape Lookout, Oregon, 225
Cape Perpetua, Oregon, 223
Carbon Glacier, Mount Rainier National
  Park, 74
Carboniferous period, 120
Carson, Washington, 192
Cascade Glaciation, 42-44
Cascade Locks, Columbia River, 192
Cascade Mountain Divide, 49
Cascade Mountains, 10, 12, 13, 14, 15, 17,
  25, 29, 45, 52, 53, 68, 95, 96, 103, 111,
  117, 120, 122, 129, 132, 136, 137, 144,
  146, 150, 159, 160, 162, 186, 188, 190,
  191, 194, 197, 215, 216, 228, 235, 238,
  251, 257, 259
Cascade Revolution, 13
Cashmere, Washington, 111
Castle Geyser, Yellowstone National
  Park, 274
"Cathedral," Oregon, 114
Catlow Valley, Oregon, 262
Catskill Mountains, 53

Caves, 84
  Arnold Ice Cave, Oregon, 87
  Clay Cave, Idaho, 88
  Cow Cave, Oregon, 158
  Crystal Falls Cave, Idaho, 87
  Formation Cave, Idaho, 88
  Hot Cave, Idaho, 88
  Ice Cave, Idaho, 88
  Kuna Cave, Idaho, 88
  Lava Caves, Mount Adams, 140
  Lava River Caves, Oregon, 171-174
  Minnetonka Cave, Idaho, 88, 89
  Oregon Caves, Oregon, 8, 84-87
  Sea Lion Caves, Oregon, 223
  Shoshone Ice Cave, Idaho, 87
  South Ice Cave, Oregon, 87
  Surveyors Ice Cave, Oregon, 87
  Trout Lake Caves, Mount Adams, 140
  Wind Cave, Idaho, 88
Cedarville, Washington, 46
Cenozoic Era, 121
Central Washington State College, 104
Centralia, Washington, 45
Cephalopods, 121
Chehalis River, Washington, 46, 222
Chelan Glacier, Washington, 43
Chelan Valley, Washington, 49, 137
Chelan, Washington, 47, 49, 50, 51, 73
Chemult, Oregon, 152
Cheney, Washington, 60, 123
Chert, 91
Chief Mountain, Montana, 37
"Chimney islands," 220
Christmas Lake, 158
Chromium oxide, 138
Chuckanut Drive, Washington, 110
Cinder cones, 136, 160
Cinders, 134, 153
Cirque-bounded peak, 14
Cirques, 16, 24, 42, 48, 64, 74, 141, 160
  snowfield, 34
Clark Fork, Idaho, 23, 53
Clark Fork River, Montana, 54, 56, 57,
  186, 261
Clark Fork Valley, Montana, 54, 55, 56,
  57, 61, 260, 261
Clarno, Oregon, 116
Clay, 1
Clay Cave, Idaho, 88
Clear Lake, Oregon, 125
Cle Elum, Washington, 103, 122
Cleft, Idaho, 264
Clepsydra Geyser, Yellowstone National
  Park, 274
Climate, temperate marine, 234
  dry continental, 234
Coal, 27, 101-103
Coast Range, 68, 96, 230
Cobbles, 118
Coeur d'Alene Lake, 55, 261
Coeur d'Alene Mountains, 57
Colorado River, 185
Colter, John, 77
Columbia basalt, 22, 67, 104, 122, 123,
  166

INDEX

Columbia Basin, 122, 143, 190, 194
Columbia County, Washington, 249
Columbia Lake, 185, 186
Columbia Plateau, 22, 23, 49, 67, 103, 123, 162-170, 188, 211, 215, 240, 249
Columbia River, 16, 22, 43, 44, 48, 49, 50, 67, 68, 69, 104, 123, 146, 162, 166, 169, 186-194, 200, 203, 207, 222, 231, 240, 253
Columbia River dunes, 240
Columbia River Gorge, 188, 190, 193, 195, 254
Columbia River Highway, 163, 194, 195, 257
Columnar basalt, 194
Columnar structure, 174,175
Colville River, Washington, 119
Composite volcano, 181-182
Concretions, 89, 90
Condon, Thomas, 95, 111, 112
Conglomerate, 3, 22, 118, 190, 192, 229
Continental Divide, 23
Cooks Chasm, Oregon, 226
Coos Bay, Oregon, 96, 103, 231
Coos Bay spit, 235
Coquille River, Oregon, 96, 220, 222, 223
Coral, 119, 120
Corvallis, Oregon, 197
Cottage Grove, Oregon, 205
Coulee City, Washington, 166
Coulee Dam, Washington, 67, 166,169, 186
Cow Cave, Oregon, 158
Cowlitz County, Washington, 110
Crater Lake National Park, 71, 107
Crater Lake, Oregon, 74, 75, 132, 148, 149, 154, 159
Craters of the Moon, Idaho, 170-181
Craters of the Moon National Monument, Idaho, 175
Crater Rock, Mount Hood, 145, 147
Cretaceous Period, 95, 98, 121
Crinoids, 119
Crown Point, Oregon, 193
Crystals, size, 5
Curlew, Washington, 121

D

Daisy Geyser, Yellowstone National Park, 274
Danskin Canyon, Idaho, 89
Dante's Inferno, Oregon Caves, 85
Davidson, Elijah J., 84
Davis Dike, Oregon, 114
Dayville, Oregon, 114, 128
Deep Creek, Washington, 111
Deer Lodge Independent, 269
Deer Lodge, Montana, 269
Denmark, Oregon, 96
Depoe Bay, Oregon, 226
Deschutes Canyon, 245
Deschutes River, Oregon, 155, 171, 197, 213, 242

Deschutes Valley, 18, 245
Deserts, 234 ff.
Devils Punch Bowl, Columbia River Highway, Oregon, 195
Devils Punch Bowl, Mount St. Helens, 144
Devonian Period, 120
Diamonds, 132, 183
Dikes, 139, 142, 160, 225
Diorite porphyry, 192
Divide, Oregon, 205
Dolomite, 39
Dome plateau, 179
Dosewallips River, Washington, 45, 197
Dragon's Head, Silent City of Rocks, Idaho, 248
Dragon's Mouth, Oregon Caves, 86
Drift, 45
Drowned river, 222
Drumlins, 32, 33
Dry Falls, Washington, 167, 168
Dunes, formation, 240-241
Dunn Mountain Road, Washington, 119
Dust, 249, 251
Dusters, 253
Dust mounds, 253
Dutton Cliff, Crater Lake, 152
Duwamish River, Washington, 47

E

Eagle Cap, 20
Eagle Creek Formation, 192, 195
Eagle Creek, Oregon, 195
Earthquake fissure, 266
Earthquake Geyser, Yellowstone National Park, 271
Earthquakes, 266 ff.
  California, 278
  Montana, 267
  Oregon, 277
  Seattle, 266
Earthquake waves, 281
Earth slides, 279
East Lake, Oregon, 155
Ecola State Park, Oregon, 220
Economic Geyser, Yellowstone National Park, 274
Eddy, Montana, 261
Eel Lake, Oregon, 233
Elephant Rock, Silent City of Rocks, Idaho, 248
Elkhorn Mountains, 18
Ellensburg Formation, Washington, 215-217
Ellensburg, Washington, 206
Elwha, 183
Elwha River, Washington, 197
Embayment, 222, 233
Emery, Montana, 269
Ennis, Montana, 273
Entiat Valley, Washington, 22, 137
Eocene Period, 96
Epoch, 93
Era, 93

INDEX

INDEX

INDEX

INDEX

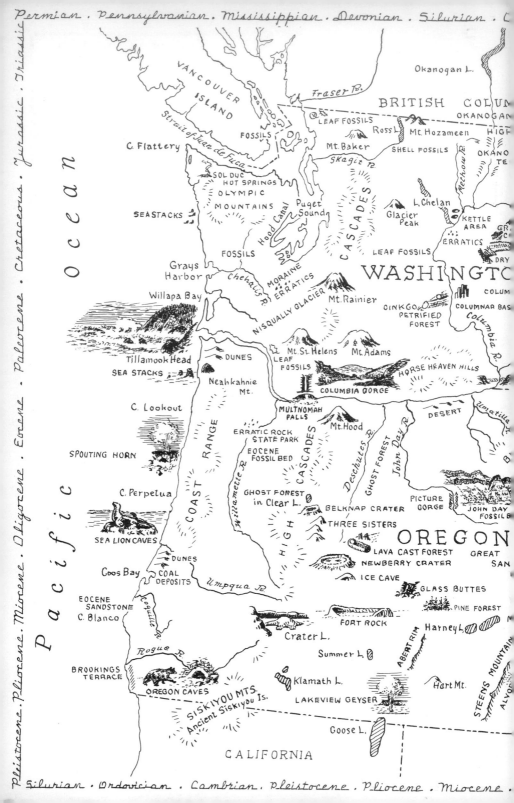